Legal Notice

ISBN-13: 978-1-951619-02-2

This is the Solution Guide to the book "Set Theory for Beginners."

Also Available from Dr. Steve Warner

CONNECT WITH DR. STEVE WARNER

www.facebook.com/SATPrepGet800

www.youtube.com/TheSATMathPrep

www.twitter.com/SATPrepGet800

www.linkedin.com/in/DrSteveWarner

www.pinterest.com/SATPrepGet800

Also Available from Dr. Steve Warner

CONNECT WITH DR. STEVE WARNER

www.facebook.com/SATPrepGet800

www.youtube.com/TheSATMathPrep

www.twitter.com/SATPrepGet800

www.linkedin.com/in/DrSteveWarner

www.pinterest.com/SATPrepGet800

Set Theory
for Beginners

Solution Guide

Dr. Steve Warner

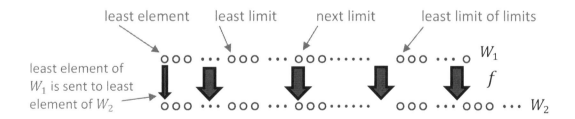

Table of Contents

Problem Set 1

LEVEL 1

1. Determine whether each of the following statements is true or false:

    (i) $k \in \{k\}$

    (ii) $0 \in \{0, 1, 2\}$

    (iii) $-1 \in \{1\}$

    (iv) $3 \in \mathbb{N}$

    (v) $-72 \in \mathbb{Z}$

Solutions:

(i) $\{k\}$ has exactly 1 element, namely k. So, $k \in \{k\}$ is **true**.

(ii) $\{0, 1, 2\}$ has exactly 3 elements, namely 0, 1, and 2. In particular, $0 \in \{0, 1, 2\}$ is **true**.

(iii) $\{1\}$ has exactly 1 element, namely 1. So, $-1 \notin \{1\}$. Therefore, $-1 \in \{1\}$ is **false**.

(iv) $\mathbb{N} = \{0, 1, 2, 3, \dots\}$. In particular, $3 \in \mathbb{N}$ is **true**.

(v) $\mathbb{Z} = \{\dots, -4, -3, -2, -1, 0, 1, 2, 3, 4, \dots\}$. In particular, $-72 \in \mathbb{Z}$ is **true**.

2. Determine the cardinality of each of the following sets:

    (i) $\{a, b, c\}$

    (ii) $\{0, 1, 2, 3, 4, 5\}$

    (iii) $\{1, 2, \dots, 72\}$

Solutions:

(i) $|\{a, b, c\}| = \mathbf{3}$.

(ii) $\{0, 1, 2, 3, 4, 5\} = 6$.

(iii) $|\{1, 2, \dots, 72\}| = \mathbf{72}$.

LEVEL 2

3. Determine whether each of the following statements is true or false:

    (i) $2 \in \emptyset$

    (ii) $\emptyset \in \{1, 2\}$

    (iii) $\emptyset \in \{\emptyset\}$

    (iv) $\{\emptyset\} \in \emptyset$

    (v) $\{\emptyset\} \in \{\emptyset\}$

Solutions:

(i)   The empty set has no elements. So, $x \in \emptyset$ is false for any x. In particular, $2 \in \emptyset$ is **false**.

(ii) $\{1, 2\}$ has exactly 2 elements, namely 1 and 2. In particular, $\emptyset \notin \{1, 2\}$. So, $\emptyset \in \{1, 2\}$ is **false**.

(iii) The set $\{\emptyset\}$ has exactly 1 element, namely $\emptyset$. So, $\emptyset \in \{\emptyset\}$ is **true**.

(iv)   The empty set has no elements. So, $x \in \emptyset$ is false for any x. In particular, $\{\emptyset\} \in \emptyset$ is **false**.

(v)   The set $\{\emptyset\}$ has 1 element, namely $\emptyset$. Since $\{\emptyset\} \neq \emptyset$, $\{\emptyset\} \in \{\emptyset\}$ is **false**.

---

4. Determine the cardinality of each of the following sets:

     (i) $\{1, 2, 3, 4, 3, 2, 1\}$

     (ii) $\{\emptyset, \{a, b, c\}\}$

     (iii) $\{3, 4, 5, \dots, 4031, 4032\}$

Solutions:

(i) $\{1, 2, 3, 4, 3, 2, 1\} = \{1, 2, 3, 4\}$. Therefore, $|\{1, 2, 3, 4, 3, 2, 1\}| = |\{1, 2, 3, 4\}| = \mathbf{4}$.

(ii) $\{\emptyset, \{a, b, c\}\}$ consists of the 2 elements $\emptyset$ and $\{a, b, c\}$. So, $|\{\emptyset, \{a, b, c\}\}| = \mathbf{2}$.

(iii) $|\{3, 4, 5, \dots, 4031, 4032\}| = 4032 - 3 + 1 = \mathbf{4030}$.

Note: For number (iii), we used the fence-post formula (see Notes 3 and 4 after Example 1.7).

LEVEL 3

5. Determine whether each of the following statements is true or false:

     (i) $\emptyset \in \emptyset$

     (ii) $\emptyset \in \{\emptyset, \{\emptyset\}\}$

     (iii) $1 \in \{2k \mid k = 1, 2, 3, 4, 5, 6\}$

     (iv) $12 \in \{3t \mid t = 1, 2, 3, 4, 5\}$

     (v) $\{a, b, c\} \in \{a, b, c\}$

Solutions:

(i)   The empty set has no elements. So, $x \in \emptyset$ is false for any x. In particular, $\emptyset \in \emptyset$ is **false**.

(ii)   The set $\{\emptyset, \{\emptyset\}\}$ has exactly 2 elements, namely $\emptyset$ and $\{\emptyset\}$. So, $\emptyset \in \{\emptyset, \{\emptyset\}\}$ is **true**.

(iii) $\{2k \mid k = 1, 2, 3, 4, 5, 6\} = \{2, 4, 6, 8, 10, 12\}$. So, $1 \notin \{2k \mid k = 1, 2, 3, 4, 5, 6\}$. Therefore, $1 \in \{2k \mid k = 1, 2, 3, 4, 5, 6\}$ is **false**.

(iv)   Since $3 \cdot 4 = 12$, $12 \in \{3t \mid t = 1, 2, 3, 4, 5\}$ is **true**.

(v)   The set $\{a, b, c\}$ has exactly 3 elements, namely a, b, and c. Since $\{a, b, c\}$ is not equal to a, b, or c, $\{a, b, c\} \in \{a, b, c\}$ is **false**.

6. Determine the cardinality of each of the following sets:

   (i) $\left\{\left\{\emptyset,\{\emptyset\}\right\}\right\}$

   (ii) $\left\{\{0,1\},\emptyset,\{\emptyset\},\{\emptyset,\{\emptyset,a,b\}\}\right\}$

   (iii) $\left\{\emptyset,\{\emptyset\},\{\{\emptyset\}\},\{\emptyset,\{\emptyset\},\{\{\emptyset\}\}\}\right\}$

Solutions:

(i) The only element of $\left\{\left\{\emptyset,\{\emptyset\}\right\}\right\}$ is $\left\{\emptyset,\{\emptyset\}\right\}$. So, $\left|\left\{\left\{\emptyset,\{\emptyset\}\right\}\right\}\right| = \mathbf{1}$.

(ii) The elements of $\left\{\{0,1\},\emptyset,\{\emptyset\},\{\emptyset,\{\emptyset,a,b\}\}\right\}$ are $\{0,1\}$, $\emptyset$, $\{\emptyset\}$, and $\{\emptyset,\{\emptyset,a,b\}\}$. So, we see that $\left|\left\{\{0,1\},\emptyset,\{\emptyset\},\{\emptyset,\{\emptyset,a,b\}\}\right\}\right| = \mathbf{4}.$

(iii) The elements of $\left\{\emptyset,\{\emptyset\},\{\{\emptyset\}\},\{\emptyset,\{\emptyset\},\{\{\emptyset\}\}\}\right\}$ are $\emptyset$, $\{\emptyset\}$, $\{\{\emptyset\}\}$, and $\{\emptyset,\{\emptyset\},\{\{\emptyset\}\}\}$. So, we see that $\left|\left\{\emptyset,\{\emptyset\},\{\{\emptyset\}\},\{\emptyset,\{\emptyset\},\{\{\emptyset\}\}\}\right\}\right| = \mathbf{4}.$

LEVEL 4

7. Determine whether each of the following statements is true or false:

   (i) $c \in \{a,\{c\}\}$

   (ii) $\{\Delta\} \in \{\delta,\Delta\}$

   (iii) $\{1\} \in \{1,a,2,b\}$

   (iv) $\emptyset \in \{\{\emptyset\}\}$

   (v) $\{\{\emptyset\}\} \in \emptyset$

Solutions:

(i) The set $\{a,\{c\}\}$ has exactly 2 elements, namely a and $\{c\}$. So, $c \in \{a,\{c\}\}$ is **false**.

(ii) The set $\{\delta,\Delta\}$ has exactly 2 elements, namely δ and Δ. So, $\{\Delta\} \in \{\delta,\Delta\}$ is **false**.

(iii) The set $\{1,a,2,b\}$ has exactly 4 elements, namely 1, a, 2 , and b. So, $\{1\} \in \{1,a,2,b\}$ is **false**.

(iv) The set $\{\{\emptyset\}\}$ has exactly 1 element, namely $\{\emptyset\}$. Since $\emptyset$ is not equal to $\{\emptyset\}$, $\emptyset \in \{\{\emptyset\}\}$ is **false**.

(v) The empty set has no elements. So, $x \in \emptyset$ is false for any x. In particular, $\{\{\emptyset\}\} \in \emptyset$ is **false**.

8. Let $C = \left\{\{\emptyset\},\{\emptyset,\{\emptyset\}\}\right\}$ and $D = \{\emptyset,\{\emptyset\}\}$. Is $C \in D$? Is $D \in C$?

Solution: The set D has exactly 2 elements, namely $\emptyset$ and $\{\emptyset\}$. So, $\boldsymbol{C \notin D}$. The set C also has exactly 2 elements, namely $\{\emptyset\}$ and $\{\emptyset,\{\emptyset\}\}$. Since $D = \{\emptyset,\{\emptyset\}\}$, $\boldsymbol{D \in C}$.

9. Determine the cardinality of $\left\{a, \{a\}, \{a, a\}, \{a, a, a, a\}, \{a, a, \{a\}\}, \{a, \{a\}, \{a\}\}\right\}$.

Solution: We have

$$\left\{a, \{a\}, \{a, a\}, \{a, a, a, a\}, \{a, a, \{a\}\}, \{a, \{a\}, \{a\}\}\right\}$$
$$= \left\{a, \{a\}, \{a\}, \{a\}, \{a, \{a\}\}, \{a, \{a\}\}\right\}$$
$$= \left\{a, \{a\}, \{a, \{a\}\}\right\}.$$

So, $\left|\left\{a, \{a\}, \{a, a\}, \{a, a, a, a\}, \{a, a, \{a\}\}, \{a, \{a\}, \{a\}\}\right\}\right| = \left|\left\{a, \{a\}, \{a, \{a\}\}\right\}\right| = \mathbf{3}$.

10. We say that a set A is **transitive** if whenever $y \in x$ and $x \in A$, it follows that $y \in A$. Determine if each of the following sets is transitive:

(i) $\emptyset$

(ii) $\{\emptyset\}$

(iii) $\{\{\emptyset\}\}$

(iv) $\{\emptyset, \{\emptyset\}\}$

(v) $\left\{\emptyset, \{\emptyset\}, \{\{\emptyset\}\}\right\}$

(vi) $\left\{\{\emptyset\}, \{\emptyset, \{\emptyset\}\}\right\}$

Solutions:

(i)   Since $\emptyset$ has no elements, $\emptyset$ **is transitive**. (The statement "whenever $x \in \emptyset$ and $y \in x$, it follows that $y \in \emptyset$" is true simply because "$x \in \emptyset$" is always false. In this case, we say that the statement is vacuously true.)

(ii)   The only element of $\{\emptyset\}$ is $\emptyset$, and $y \in \emptyset$ is always false. So, $\{\emptyset\}$ **is transitive**.

(iii) $\{\emptyset\} \in \{\{\emptyset\}\}$ and $\emptyset \in \{\emptyset\}$, but $\emptyset \notin \{\{\emptyset\}\}$. So, $\{\{\emptyset\}\}$ **is not transitive**.

(iv) $\{\emptyset, \{\emptyset\}\}$ has 2 elements, namely $\emptyset$ and $\{\emptyset\}$. $y \in \emptyset$ is always false. The only element of $\{\emptyset\}$ is $\emptyset$, and $\emptyset \in \{\emptyset, \{\emptyset\}\}$. It follows that $\{\emptyset, \{\emptyset\}\}$ **is transitive**.

(v) $\left\{\emptyset, \{\emptyset\}, \{\{\emptyset\}\}\right\}$ has 3 elements, namely $\emptyset$, $\{\emptyset\}$, and $\{\{\emptyset\}\}$. $y \in \emptyset$ is always false. The only element of $\{\emptyset\}$ is $\emptyset$, and $\emptyset \in \left\{\emptyset, \{\emptyset\}, \{\{\emptyset\}\}\right\}$. The only element of $\{\{\emptyset\}\}$ is $\{\emptyset\}$, and $\{\emptyset\} \in \left\{\emptyset, \{\emptyset\}, \{\{\emptyset\}\}\right\}$. It follows that $\left\{\emptyset, \{\emptyset\}, \{\{\emptyset\}\}\right\}$ **is transitive**.

(vi) $\{\emptyset\} \in \left\{\{\emptyset\}, \{\emptyset, \{\emptyset\}\}\right\}$ and $\emptyset \in \{\emptyset\}$, but $\emptyset \notin \left\{\{\emptyset\}, \{\emptyset, \{\emptyset\}\}\right\}$. So, $\left\{\{\emptyset\}, \{\emptyset, \{\emptyset\}\}\right\}$ **is not transitive**.

Problem Set 2

LEVEL 1

1. Determine whether each of the following statements is true or false:

   (i) $\emptyset \subseteq \{a, b\}$

   (ii) $\{\Delta\} \subseteq \{\delta, \Delta\}$

   (iii) $\{1, 2, 3\} \subseteq \{1, 2, 3\}$

   (iv) $\{1, c, \{5, k\}\} \subseteq \{1, c, 5, k\}$

Solutions:

(i)   The empty set is a subset of every set. So, $\emptyset \subseteq \{a, b\}$ is **true**.

(ii) The only element of $\{\Delta\}$ is Δ. Since Δ is also an element of $\{\delta, \Delta\}$, $\{\Delta\} \subseteq \{\delta, \Delta\}$ is **true**.

(iii) Every set is a subset of itself. So, $\{1, 2, 3\} \subseteq \{1, 2, 3\}$ is **true**.

(iv) $\{5, k\} \in \{1, c, \{5, k\}\}$, but $\{5, k\} \notin \{1, c, 5, k\}$. So, $\{1, c, \{5, k\}\} \subseteq \{1, c, 5, k\}$ is **false**.

2. Provide a single example of a set A with the following properties: (i) $A \subset \mathbb{Z}$ (A is a *proper* subset of $\mathbb{Z}$); (ii) A is infinite; (iii) A contains both positive and negative integers; (iv) A contains both even and odd integers.

Solution: One example of such a set A is $A = \{\ldots, -6, -4, -2, 1, 3, 5, \ldots\}$.

LEVEL 2

3. Determine whether each of the following statements is true or false:

   (i) $\emptyset \subseteq \emptyset$

   (ii) $\emptyset \subseteq \{\emptyset\}$

   (iii) $\{\emptyset\} \subseteq \emptyset$

   (iv) $\{\emptyset\} \subseteq \{\emptyset\}$

Solutions:

(i)   The empty set is a subset of every set. So, $\emptyset \subseteq X$ is true for any X. In particular, $\emptyset \subseteq \emptyset$ is **true**. (This can also be done by using the fact that every set is a subset of itself.)

(ii) Again, (as in (i)), $\emptyset \subseteq X$ is true for any X. In particular, $\emptyset \subseteq \{\emptyset\}$ is **true**.

(iii) The only subset of $\emptyset$ is $\emptyset$. So, $\{\emptyset\} \subseteq \emptyset$ is **false**.

(iv) Every set is a subset of itself. So, $\{\emptyset\} \subseteq \{\emptyset\}$ is **true**.

4. Compute the power set of each of the following sets:

    (i) $\emptyset$

    (ii) $\{\delta, \Delta\}$

    (iii) $\{\emptyset, \{\emptyset\}\}$

    (iv) $\{\{\emptyset\}\}$

Solutions:

  (i) $\mathcal{P}(\emptyset) = \{\emptyset\}$

  (ii) $\mathcal{P}(\{\delta, \Delta\}) = \{\emptyset, \{\delta\}, \{\Delta\}, \{\delta, \Delta\}\}$

  (iii) $\mathcal{P}(\{\emptyset, \{\emptyset\}\}) = \{\emptyset, \{\emptyset\}, \{\{\emptyset\}\}, \{\emptyset, \{\emptyset\}\}\}$

  (iv) $\mathcal{P}(\{\{\emptyset\}\}) = \{\emptyset, \{\{\emptyset\}\}\}$

LEVEL 3

5. How many subsets does $\{a, b, c, d\}$ have? Draw a tree diagram for the subsets of $\{a, b, c, d\}$.

Solution: $|\{a, b, c, d\}| = 4$. Therefore, $\{a, b, c, d\}$ has $2^4 = \mathbf{16}$ subsets. We can also say that the size of the power set of $\{a, b, c, d\}$ is 16, that is, $|\mathcal{P}(\{a, b, c, d\})| = 16$. Here is a tree diagram.

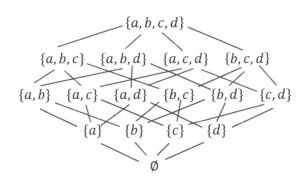

6. Let A, B, C, D, and E be sets such that $A \subseteq B$, $B \subseteq C$, $C \subseteq D$, and $D \subseteq E$. Prove that $A \subseteq E$.

Proof: Suppose that A, B, C, D, and E are sets such that $A \subseteq B$, $B \subseteq C$, $C \subseteq D$, and $D \subseteq E$. Since $A \subseteq B$ and $B \subseteq C$, by Theorem 2.3, we have $A \subseteq C$. Since $A \subseteq C$ and $C \subseteq D$, again by Theorem 2.3, we have $A \subseteq D$. Finally, since $A \subseteq D$ and $D \subseteq E$, once again by Theorem 2.3, we have $A \subseteq E$. $\qquad\square$

LEVEL 4

7. A relation R is **reflexive** if $\forall x (xRx)$ and **symmetric** if $\forall x \forall y (xRy \rightarrow yRx)$. For example, the relation "=" is reflexive and symmetric because $\forall x (x = x)$ and $\forall x \forall y (x = y \rightarrow y = x)$. Show that $\subseteq$ is reflexive, but $\in$ is not. Then decide if each of $\subseteq$ and $\in$ is symmetric.

Solutions: ($\subseteq$ **is reflexive**) Let A be a set. By Theorem 2.1, A is a subset of itself. So, $A \subseteq A$ is true. Since A was arbitrary, $\forall x(A \subseteq A)$ is true. Therefore, $\subseteq$ is reflexive. □

($\in$ is **not** reflexive) Since the empty set has no elements, $\emptyset \notin \emptyset$. This **counterexample** shows that $\in$ is not reflexive.

($\subseteq$ is **not** symmetric) $\{1\} \subseteq \{1,2\}$, but $\{1,2\} \nsubseteq \{1\}$. This **counterexample** shows that $\subseteq$ is not symmetric.

($\in$ is **not** symmetric) $\emptyset \in \{\emptyset\}$, but $\{\emptyset\} \notin \emptyset$. This **counterexample** shows that $\in$ is not symmetric.

Note: A **conjecture** is an educated guess. In math, conjectures are made all the time based upon evidence from examples (but examples alone cannot be used to prove a conjecture). A logical argument is usually needed to prove a conjecture, whereas a single **counterexample** is used to disprove a conjecture. For example, $\emptyset \notin \emptyset$ is a counterexample to the conjecture "$\in$ is reflexive."

8. A set A is transitive if $\forall x(x \in A \rightarrow x \subseteq A)$ (in words, every element of A is also a subset of A). Prove that if A is a transitive set, then $\mathcal{P}(A)$ is also a transitive set.

Proof: Let A be a transitive set, let $x \in \mathcal{P}(A)$, and let $y \in x$. Since $x \in \mathcal{P}(A)$, $x \subseteq A$. Since $y \in x$ and $x \subseteq A$, $y \in A$. Since A is transitive and $y \in A$, $y \subseteq A$. So, $y \in \mathcal{P}(A)$. Since $y \in x$ was arbitrary, $\forall y(y \in x \rightarrow y \in \mathcal{P}(A))$. Therefore, $x \subseteq \mathcal{P}(A)$. Since x was arbitrary, $\forall x(x \in \mathcal{P}(A) \rightarrow x \subseteq \mathcal{P}(A))$. Thus, $\mathcal{P}(A)$ is transitive. □

LEVEL 5

9. Let $P(x)$ be the property $x \notin x$. Prove that $\{x|P(x)\}$ cannot be a set.

Solution: Suppose toward contradiction that $A = \{x \mid x \notin x\}$ is a set. Then $A \in A$ if and only if $A \notin A$. So, $p \leftrightarrow \neg p$ is true, where p is the statement $A \in A$. However, $p \leftrightarrow \neg p$ is always false. This is a contradiction. So, A is not a set. □

Notes: (1) This is our first **proof by contradiction**. A proof by contradiction works as follows:

1. We assume the negation of what we are trying to prove.

2. We use a logically sound argument to derive a statement which is false.

3. Since the argument is logically sound, the only possible error is our original assumption. Therefore, the negation of our original assumption must be true.

In this problem we are trying to prove that $A = \{x \mid x \notin x\}$ **is not** a set. The negation of this statement is that $A = \{x \mid x \notin x\}$ **is** a set. We then use only the definition of A to get the false statement $A \in A \leftrightarrow \neg A \in A$. Since the argument was logically valid, our initial assumption must have been incorrect, and therefore, A is not a set.

13

(2) The contradiction that occurs here is known as **Russell's Paradox**. This contradiction shows that we need to be careful about how we define a set. A naïve definition would be that a set is any object that has the form $\{x|P(x)\}$, where $P(x)$ is an arbitrary property (by property, we mean a **first-order property**—this is a property defined using the connectives $\wedge$, $\vee$, $\rightarrow$, and $\leftrightarrow$, the quantifiers $\forall$ and $\exists$, and the relations $=$ and $\in$—see Lesson 10 for details). As we see in this problem, that "definition" of a set leads to a contradiction. Instead, we call $\{x|P(x)\}$ a **class**. Every set is a class, but not every class is a set. A class that is not a set is called a **proper class**. For example, $\{x|x \notin x\}$ is a proper class.

10. Let $A = \{a, b, c, d\}$, $B = \{X \mid X \subseteq A \wedge d \notin X\}$, and $C = \{X \mid X \subseteq A \wedge d \in X\}$. Show that there is a natural **one-to-one correspondence** (see definition below) between the elements of B and the elements of C. Then generalize this result to a set with $n + 1$ elements for $n > 0$.

Definition: Informally, a **one-to-one correspondence** between two sets is a pairing so that each element of the first set is matched up with exactly one element of the second set, and vice versa.

Formally, a **one-to-one correspondence** is a function that is bijective. Functions (and in particular, bijective functions) will be defined rigorously in Lesson 6.

Solution: We define the one-to-one correspondence as follows: If $Y \in B$, then Y is a subset of A that does not contain d. Let Y_d be the set that contains the same elements as Y, but with d thrown in. Then the correspondence $Y \rightarrow Y_d$ is a one-to-one correspondence. We can see this correspondence in the table below.

Elements of B	Elements of C
$\emptyset$	$\{d\}$
$\{a\}$	$\{a, d\}$
$\{b\}$	$\{b, d\}$
$\{c\}$	$\{c, d\}$
$\{a, b\}$	$\{a, b, d\}$
$\{a, c\}$	$\{a, c, d\}$
$\{b, c\}$	$\{b, c, d\}$
$\{a, b, c\}$	$\{a, b, c, d\}$

For the general result, we start with a set A with $n + 1$ elements, and we let d be some element from A. Define B and C the same way as before: $B = \{X \mid X \subseteq A \wedge d \notin X\}$, and $C = \{X \mid X \subseteq A \wedge d \in X\}$. Also, as before, if $Y \in B$, then Y is a subset of A that does not contain d. Let Y_d be the set that contains the same elements as Y, but with d thrown in. Then the correspondence $Y \rightarrow Y_d$ is a one-to-one correspondence.

Notes: (1) B consists of the subsets of A that do not contain the element d, while C consists of the subsets of A that do contain d.

(2) Observe that in the case where $A = \{a, b, c, d\}$, B and C each have $8 = 2^3$ elements. Also, there is no overlap between B and C (they have no elements in common). So, we have a total of $8 + 8 = 16$ elements. Since there are exactly $2^4 = 16$ subsets of A, we see that we have listed every subset of A.

(3) We could also do the computation in Note 2 as follows: $2^3 + 2^3 = 2 \cdot 2^3 = 2^1 \cdot 2^3 = 2^{1+3} = 2^4$. It's nice to see the computation this way because it mimics the computation we will do in the more general case. In case your algebra skills are not that strong, here is an explanation of each step:

Adding the same thing to itself is equivalent to multiplying that thing by 2. For example, 1 apple plus 1 apple is 2 apples. Similarly, $1x + 1x = 2x$. This could be written more briefly as $x + x = 2x$. Replacing x by 2^3 gives us $2^3 + 2^3 = 2 \cdot 2^3$ (the first equality in the computation above).

Next, by definition, $x^1 = x$. So, $2^1 = 2$. Therefore, we can rewrite $2 \cdot 2^3$ as $2^1 \cdot 2^3$.

Now, 2^3 means to multiply 2 by itself 3 times. So, $2^3 = 2 \cdot 2 \cdot 2$. Thus, $2^1 \cdot 2^3 = 2 \cdot 2 \cdot 2 \cdot 2 = 2^4$. This leads to the rule of exponents which says that if you multiply two expressions with the same base, you can add the exponents. So, $2^1 \cdot 2^3 = 2^{1+3} = 2^4$.

(4) In the more general case, B and C each have 2^n elements. The reason for this is that A has $n + 1$ elements. When we remove the element d from A, the resulting set has n elements, and therefore, 2^n subsets. B consists of precisely the subsets of this new set (A with d removed), and so, B has exactly 2^n elements. The one-to-one correspondence $Y \to Y_d$ shows that C has the same number of elements as B. Therefore, C also has 2^n elements.

(5) In the general case, there is still no overlap between B and C. It follows that the total number of elements when we combine B and C is $2^n + 2^n = 2 \cdot 2^n = 2^1 \cdot 2^n = 2^{1+n} = 2^{n+1}$. See Note 3 above for an explanation as to how all this algebra works.

(6) By a **one-to-one correspondence** between the elements of B and the elements of C, we mean a pairing where we match each element of B with exactly one element of C so that each element of C is matched with exactly one element of B. The table given in the solution above provides a nice example of such a pairing.

(7) In the case where $A = \{a, b, c, d\}$, B consists of all the subsets of $\{a, b, c\}$. In other words, $B = \{X \mid X \subseteq \{a, b, c\}\} = \mathcal{P}(\{a, b, c\})$.

A description of C is a bit more complicated. It consists of the subsets of $\{a, b, c\}$ with d thrown into them. We could write this as $C = \{X \cup \{d\} \mid X \subseteq \{a, b, c\}\}$.

(5) In the general case, we can write $K = A \setminus \{d\}$ (this is the set consisting of all the elements of A, except d). We then have $B = \{X \mid X \subseteq K\} = \mathcal{P}(K)$ and $C = \{X \cup \{d\} \mid X \subseteq K\} = \mathcal{P}(A) \setminus \mathcal{P}(K)$.

(6) The symbol "$\setminus$" for **set difference** will be defined formally in Lesson 3.

LEVEL 1

1. Let $A = \{a, b, \Delta, \delta\}$ and $B = \{b, c, \delta, \gamma\}$. Determine each of the following:

   (i) $A \cup B$

   (ii) $A \cap B$

   (iii) $A \setminus B$

   (iv) $B \setminus A$

   (v) $A \,\Delta\, B$

Solutions:

(i) $A \cup B = \{a, b, c, \Delta, \delta, \gamma\}$.

(ii) $A \cap B = \{b, \delta\}$.

(iii) $A \setminus B = \{a, \Delta\}$

(iv) $B \setminus A = \{c, \gamma\}$

(v) $A \,\Delta\, B = \{a, \Delta\} \cup \{c, \gamma\} = \{a, c, \Delta, \gamma\}$

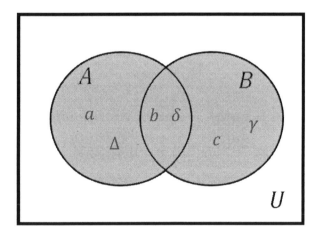

2. Draw Venn diagrams for $(A \setminus B) \setminus C$ and $A \setminus (B \setminus C)$. Are these two sets equal for all sets A, B, and C? If so, prove it. If not, provide a counterexample.

Solution:

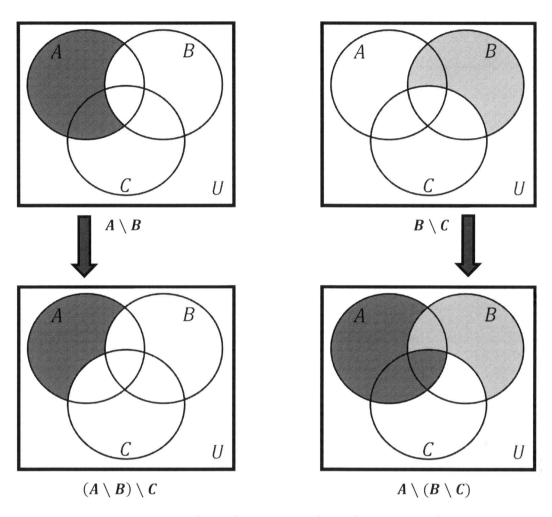

From the Venn diagrams, it looks like $(A \setminus B) \setminus C \subseteq A \setminus (B \setminus C)$, but $(A \setminus B) \setminus C \neq A \setminus (B \setminus C)$.

Let's come up with a counterexample. Let $A = \{1, 2\}$, $B = \{1, 3\}$, and $C = \{1, 4\}$. Then we have $(A \setminus B) \setminus C = \{2\} \setminus \{1, 4\} = \{2\}$ and $A \setminus (B \setminus C) = \{1, 2\} \setminus \{3\} = \{1, 2\}$.

We see that $(A \setminus B) \setminus C \neq A \setminus (B \setminus C)$.

Note: Although it was not asked in the question, let's prove that $(A \setminus B) \setminus C \subseteq A \setminus (B \setminus C)$. Let $x \in (A \setminus B) \setminus C$. Then $x \in A \setminus B$ and $x \notin C$. Since $x \in A \setminus B$, $x \in A$ and $x \notin B$. In particular, $x \in A$. Since $x \notin B$, $x \notin B \setminus C$ (because if $x \in B \setminus C$, then $x \in B$). So, we have $x \in A$ and $x \notin B \setminus C$. Therefore, $x \in A \setminus (B \setminus C)$. Since $x \in (A \setminus B) \setminus C$ was arbitrary, $(A \setminus B) \setminus C \subseteq A \setminus (B \setminus C)$. $\quad\square$

3. Let $A = \left\{\emptyset, \{\emptyset, \{\emptyset\}\}\right\}$ and $B = \{\emptyset, \{\emptyset\}\}$. Compute each of the following:

      (i) $A \cup B$

      (ii) $A \cap B$

      (iii) $A \setminus B$

      (iv) $B \setminus A$

      (v) $A \, \Delta \, B$

Solutions:

(i) $A \cup B = \left\{\emptyset, \{\emptyset\}, \{\emptyset, \{\emptyset\}\}\right\}$.

(ii) $A \cap B = \{\emptyset\}$.

(iii) $A \setminus B = \left\{\{\emptyset, \{\emptyset\}\}\right\}$

(iv) $B \setminus A = \{\{\emptyset\}\}$

(v) $A \, \Delta \, B = \left\{\{\emptyset, \{\emptyset\}\}\right\} \cup \{\{\emptyset\}\} = \left\{\{\emptyset\}, \{\emptyset, \{\emptyset\}\}\right\}$

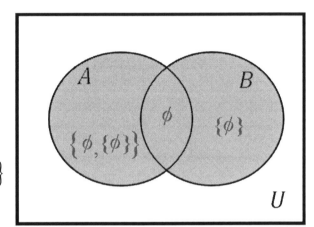

4. Prove the following:

      (i)   The operation of forming unions is commutative.

      (ii)   The operation of forming intersections is commutative.

      (iii) The operation of forming intersections is associative.

Proofs:

(i)   Let A and B be sets. Then $x \in A \cup B$ if and only if $x \in A$ or $x \in B$ if and only if $x \in B$ or $x \in A$ if and only if $x \in B \cup A$. Since x was arbitrary, we have shown $\forall x(x \in A \cup B \leftrightarrow x \in B \cup A)$. Therefore, $A \cup B = B \cup A$. So, the operation of forming unions is commutative. $\quad\square$

(ii)   Let A and B be sets. Then $x \in A \cap B$ if and only if $x \in A$ and $x \in B$ if and only if $x \in B$ and $x \in A$ if and only if $x \in B \cap A$. Since x was arbitrary, we have $\forall x(x \in A \cap B \leftrightarrow x \in B \cap A)$. Therefore, $A \cap B = B \cap A$. So, the operation of forming intersections is commutative. $\quad\square$

(iii) Let A, B, and C be sets. Then $x \in (A \cap B) \cap C$ if and only if $x \in A \cap B$ and $x \in C$ if and only if $x \in A$, $x \in B$ and $x \in C$ if and only if $x \in A$ and $x \in B \cap C$ if and only if $x \in A \cap (B \cap C)$. Since x was arbitrary, we have shown $\forall x\big(x \in (A \cap B) \cap C \leftrightarrow x \in A \cap (B \cap C)\big)$.

    Therefore, we have shown that $(A \cap B) \cap C = A \cap (B \cap C)$. So, the operation of forming intersections is associative. $\quad\square$

LEVEL 3

5. Prove or provide a counterexample:

    (i)   Every pairwise disjoint set of sets is disjoint.

    (ii)   Every disjoint set of sets is pairwise disjoint.

Solutions:

  (i)   This is **false**. Let $A = \{1\}$ and let $X = \{A\}$. X is pairwise disjoint, but $\cap X = A = \{1\} \neq \emptyset$.

       However, the following slightly modified statement is **true**: "Every pairwise disjoint set of sets consisting of at least two sets is disjoint."

       Let X be a pairwise disjoint set of sets with at least two sets, say $A, B \in X$. Suppose towards contradiction that $x \in \cap X$. Then $x \in A$ and $x \in B$. So, $x \in A \cap B$. But $A \cap B = \emptyset$ because X is pairwise disjoint. This contradiction shows that the statement $x \in \cap X$ is false. Therefore, X is disjoint. $\qquad\square$

  (ii)   This is **false**. Let $A = \{0,1\}$, $B = \{1,2\}$, $C = \{0,2\}$, and $X = \{A, B, C\}$. Then X is disjoint because $\cap X = A \cap B \cap C = \{0,1\} \cap \{1,2\} \cap \{0,2\} = \{1\} \cap \{0,2\} = \emptyset$. However, X is **not** pairwise disjoint because $A \cap B = \{0,1\} \cap \{1,2\} = \{1\} \neq \emptyset$.

6. Let A and B be sets. Prove that $A \cap B \subseteq A$.

Proof: Suppose that A and B are sets and let $x \in A \cap B$. Then $x \in A$ and $x \in B$. In particular, $x \in A$. Since x was an arbitrary element of A, we have shown that every element of $A \cap B$ is an element of A. That is, $\forall x(x \in A \cap B \rightarrow x \in A)$ is true. Therefore, $A \cap B \subseteq A$. $\qquad\square$

LEVEL 4

7. Prove that $B \subseteq A$ if and only if $A \cap B = B$.

Proof: Suppose that $B \subseteq A$. By part (ii) of Problem 4 and Problem 6, $A \cap B = B \cap A \subseteq B$. Let $x \in B$. Since $B \subseteq A$, $x \in A$. Therefore, $x \in A$ and $x \in B$. So, $x \in A \cap B$. Since x was an arbitrary element of B, we have shown that every element of B is an element of $A \cap B$. That is, $\forall x(x \in B \rightarrow x \in A \cap B)$. Therefore, $B \subseteq A \cap B$. Since $A \cap B \subseteq B$ and $B \subseteq A \cap B$, it follows that $A \cap B = B$.

Now, suppose that $A \cap B = B$ and let $x \in B$. Then $x \in A \cap B$. So, $x \in A$ and $x \in B$. In particular, $x \in A$. Since x was an arbitrary element of B, we have shown that every element of B is an element of A. That is, $\forall x(x \in B \rightarrow x \in A)$. Therefore, $B \subseteq A$. $\qquad\square$

8. Let A, B, and C be sets. Prove each of the following:

    (i) $A \cap (B \cup C) = (A \cap B) \cup (A \cap C)$.

    (ii) $A \cup (B \cap C) = (A \cup B) \cap (A \cup C)$.

    (iii) $C \setminus (A \cup B) = (C \setminus A) \cap (C \setminus B)$.

    (iv) $C \setminus (A \cap B) = (C \setminus A) \cup (C \setminus B)$.

Proofs:

(i) $x \in A \cap (B \cup C) \Leftrightarrow x \in A$ and $x \in B \cup C \Leftrightarrow x \in A$ and either $x \in B$ or $x \in C \Leftrightarrow x \in A$ and $x \in B$ or $x \in A$ and $x \in C \Leftrightarrow x \in A \cap B$ or $x \in A \cap C \Leftrightarrow x \in (A \cap B) \cup (A \cap C)$. $\square$

(ii) $x \in A \cup (B \cap C) \Leftrightarrow x \in A$ or $x \in B \cap C \Leftrightarrow$ either $x \in A$ or we have both $x \in B$ and $x \in C \Leftrightarrow$ we have both $x \in A$ or $x \in B$ and $x \in A$ or $x \in C \Leftrightarrow x \in A \cup B$ and $x \in A \cup C \Leftrightarrow x \in (A \cup B) \cap (A \cup C)$. $\square$

(iii) $x \in C \setminus (A \cup B) \Leftrightarrow x \in C$ and $x \notin A \cup B \Leftrightarrow x \in C$ and $x \notin A$ and $x \notin B \Leftrightarrow x \in C$ and $x \notin A$ and $x \in C$ and $x \notin B \Leftrightarrow x \in C \setminus A$ and $x \in C \setminus B \Leftrightarrow x \in (C \setminus A) \cap (C \setminus B)$. $\square$

(iv) $x \in C \setminus (A \cap B) \Leftrightarrow x \in C$ and $x \notin A \cap B \Leftrightarrow x \in C$ and $x \notin A$ or $x \notin B \Leftrightarrow x \in C$ and $x \notin A$ or $x \in C$ and $x \notin B \Leftrightarrow x \in C \setminus A$ or $x \in C \setminus B \Leftrightarrow x \in (C \setminus A) \cup (C \setminus B)$. $\square$

Notes: Let's let p, q, and r be the statements $x \in A$, $x \in B$, and $x \in C$, respectively.

(1) In (i) above, the statement "$x \in A$ and either $x \in B$ or $x \in C$" can be written $p \wedge (q \vee r)$. It can be shown that this is equivalent to $(p \wedge q) \vee (p \wedge r)$ (for example, draw the truth tables). In words, this is the statement "$x \in A$ and $x \in B$ or $x \in A$ and $x \in C$." Here it needs to be understood that the word "and" takes precedence over the word "or."

Similarly, we can use the logical equivalence $p \vee (q \wedge r) \equiv (p \vee q) \wedge (p \vee r)$ to help understand the proof of (ii).

(2) The equivalences $p \wedge (q \vee r) \equiv (p \wedge q) \vee (p \wedge r)$ and $p \vee (q \wedge r) \equiv (p \vee q) \wedge (p \vee r)$ are known as the **distributive laws**.

The rules $A \cap (B \cup C) = (A \cap B) \cup (A \cap C)$ and $A \cup (B \cap C) = (A \cup B) \cap (A \cup C)$ are also known as the **distributive laws**.

(3) To clarify (iii) and (iv), note that $\neg(p \vee q) \equiv \neg p \wedge \neg q$ and $\neg(p \wedge q) \equiv \neg p \vee \neg q$ (these equivalences can be easily checked). These two equivalences are known as **De Morgan's laws**. For (iii), we can use the logical equivalence $\neg(p \vee q) \equiv \neg p \wedge \neg q$ with p the statement $x \in A$ and q the statement $x \in B$ to get

$$x \notin A \cup B \equiv \neg x \in A \cup B \equiv \neg(x \in A \vee x \in B) \equiv \neg(p \vee q) \equiv \neg p \wedge \neg q \text{ (by De Morgan's law)}$$
$$\equiv \neg x \in A \wedge \neg x \in B \equiv x \notin A \wedge x \notin B.$$

So, the statement "$x \in C$ and $x \notin A \cup B$" is equivalent to $x \in C \wedge x \notin A \wedge x \notin B$.

Similarly, we can use the logical equivalence $\neg(p \wedge q) \equiv \neg p \vee \neg q$ to see that the statement "$x \in C$ and $x \notin A \cap B$" is equivalent to "$x \in C$ and $x \notin A$ or $x \notin B$."

(4) The rules $C \setminus (A \cup B) = (C \setminus A) \cap (C \setminus B)$ and $C \setminus (A \cap B) = (C \setminus A) \cup (C \setminus B)$ are also known as **De Morgan's laws**.

9. Let X be a nonempty set of sets. Prove the following:

    (i)   For all $A \in X$, $A \subseteq \bigcup X$.

    (ii)   For all $A \in X$, $\bigcap X \subseteq A$.

Proofs:

(i)   Let X be a nonempty set of sets, let $A \in X$, and let $x \in A$. Then there is $B \in X$ such that $x \in B$ (namely A). So, $x \in \bigcup X$. Since x was an arbitrary element of A, we have shown that $A \subseteq \bigcup X$. Since A was an arbitrary element of X, we have shown that for all $A \in X$, we have $A \subseteq \bigcup X$.   □

(ii)   Let X be a nonempty set of sets, let $A \in X$, and let $x \in \bigcap X$. Then for every $B \in X$, we have $x \in B$. In particular, $x \in A$ (because $A \in X$). Since x was an arbitrary element of $\bigcap X$, we have shown that $\bigcap X \subseteq A$. Since A was an arbitrary element of X, we have shown that for all $A \in X$, we have $\bigcap X \subseteq A$.   □

10. Let A be a set and let X be a nonempty collection of sets. Prove each of the following:

    (i) $A \cap \bigcup X = \bigcup \{A \cap B \mid B \in X\}$

    (ii) $A \cup \bigcap X = \bigcap \{A \cup B \mid B \in X\}$

    (iii) $A \setminus \bigcup X = \bigcap \{A \setminus B \mid B \in X\}$

    (iv) $A \setminus \bigcap X = \bigcup \{A \setminus B \mid B \in X\}$.

Proofs:

(i) $x \in A \cap \bigcup X \Leftrightarrow x \in A$ and $x \in \bigcup X \Leftrightarrow x \in A$ and there is a $B \in X$ with $x \in B \Leftrightarrow x \in A \cap B$ for some $B \in X \Leftrightarrow x \in \bigcup \{A \cap B \mid B \in X\}$.   □

(ii) $x \in A \cup \bigcap X \Leftrightarrow x \in A$ or $x \in \bigcap X \Leftrightarrow x \in A$ or $x \in B$ for every $B \in X \Leftrightarrow x \in A \cup B$ for every $B \in X \Leftrightarrow x \in \bigcap \{A \cup B \mid B \in X\}$.   □

(iii) $x \in A \setminus \bigcup X \Leftrightarrow x \in A$ and $x \notin \bigcup X \Leftrightarrow x \in A$ and $x \notin B$ for every $B \in X \Leftrightarrow x \in A \setminus B$ for every $B \in X \Leftrightarrow x \in \bigcap \{A \setminus B \mid B \in X\}$.   □

(iv) $x \in A \setminus \bigcap X \Leftrightarrow x \in A$ and $x \notin \bigcap X \Leftrightarrow x \in A$ and $x \notin B$ for some $B \in X \Leftrightarrow x \in A \setminus B$ for some $B \in X \Leftrightarrow x \in \bigcup \{A \setminus B \mid B \in X\}$.   □

Note: The rules in (i) and (ii) are known as the **generalized distributive laws** and the rules in (iii) and (iv) are known as the **generalized De Morgan's laws.**

Problem Set 4

LEVEL 1

1. List the elements of $\{\Delta, \gamma, \tau\} \times \{z, t\}$.

Solution: $(\Delta, z), (\Delta, t), (\gamma, z), (\gamma, t), (\tau, z), (\tau, t)$

2. For each set A below, evaluate (i) A^2; (ii) A^3; (iii) $\mathcal{P}(A)$.
   $$1.\ A = \emptyset \quad 2.\ A = \{\emptyset\} \quad 3.\ A = \mathcal{P}(\{\emptyset\})$$

Solutions:

(i) $\emptyset^2 = \emptyset \times \emptyset = \emptyset$.

  $\{\emptyset\}^2 = \{\emptyset\} \times \{\emptyset\} = \{(\emptyset, \emptyset)\}$.

  Since $\mathcal{P}(\{\emptyset\}) = \{\emptyset, \{\emptyset\}\}$, we have
  $$\mathcal{P}(\{\emptyset\})^2 = \mathcal{P}(\{\emptyset\}) \times \mathcal{P}(\{\emptyset\}) = \{(\emptyset, \emptyset), (\emptyset, \{\emptyset\}), (\{\emptyset\}, \emptyset), (\{\emptyset\}, \{\emptyset\})\}.$$

(ii) $\emptyset^3 = \emptyset \times \emptyset \times \emptyset = \emptyset$.

  $\{\emptyset\}^3 = \{\emptyset\} \times \{\emptyset\} \times \{\emptyset\} = \{(\emptyset, \emptyset, \emptyset)\}$.

  Since $\mathcal{P}(\{\emptyset\}) = \{\emptyset, \{\emptyset\}\}$, we have $\mathcal{P}(\{\emptyset\})^3 = \mathcal{P}(\{\emptyset\}) \times \mathcal{P}(\{\emptyset\}) \times \mathcal{P}(\{\emptyset\})$

$= \{(\emptyset, \emptyset, \emptyset), (\emptyset, \emptyset, \{\emptyset\}), (\emptyset, \{\emptyset\}, \emptyset), (\emptyset, \{\emptyset\}, \{\emptyset\}), (\{\emptyset\}, \emptyset, \emptyset), (\{\emptyset\}, \emptyset, \{\emptyset\}), (\{\emptyset\}, \{\emptyset\}, \emptyset), (\{\emptyset\}, \{\emptyset\}, \{\emptyset\})\}$

(iii) $\mathcal{P}(\emptyset) = \{\emptyset\}$

  $\mathcal{P}(\{\emptyset\}) = \{\emptyset, \{\emptyset\}\}$

  Since $\mathcal{P}(\{\emptyset\}) = \{\emptyset, \{\emptyset\}\}$, we have $\mathcal{P}\big(\mathcal{P}(\{\emptyset\})\big) = \Big\{\emptyset, \{\emptyset\}, \{\{\emptyset\}\}, \{\emptyset, \{\emptyset\}\}\Big\}$.

LEVEL 2

3. Compute each of the following:
   (i) $\{0, 1, 2\}^3$
   (ii) $\{a, b\}^4$

Solutions:

(i) $\{0, 1, 2\}^3 = \{0, 1, 2\} \times \{0, 1, 2\} \times \{0, 1, 2\} = \{(0, 0, 0), (0, 0, 1), (0, 0, 2), (0, 1, 0), (0, 1, 1),$
$(0, 1, 2), (0, 2, 0), (0, 2, 1), (0, 2, 2), (1, 0, 0), (1, 0, 1), (1, 0, 2), (1, 1, 0), (1, 1, 1), (1, 1, 2),$
$(1, 2, 0), (1, 2, 1), (1, 2, 2), (2, 0, 0), (2, 0, 1), (2, 0, 2), (2, 1, 0), (2, 1, 1), (2, 1, 2), (2, 2, 0),$
$(2, 2, 1), (2, 2, 2)\}$.

(ii) $\{a, b\}^4 = \{a, b\} \times \{a, b\} \times \{a, b\} \times \{a, b\} = \{(a, a, a, a), (a, a, a, b), (a, a, b, a), (a, a, b, b),$
$(a, b, a, a), (a, b, a, b), (a, b, b, a), (a, b, b, b), (b, a, a, a), (b, a, a, b), (b, a, b, a), (b, a, b, b),$
$(b, b, a, a), (b, b, a, b), (b, b, b, a), (b, b, b, b)\},$

4. Find the domain, range, and field of each of the following relations:

    (i) $R = \{(a, b), (c, d), (e, f), (f, a)\}$

    (ii) $S = \{(2k, 2t + 1) \mid k, t \in \mathbb{Z}\}$

Solutions:

(i) $\operatorname{dom} R = \{a, c, e, f\}$; $\operatorname{ran} R = \{a, b, d, f\}$; field $R = \{a, b, c, d, e, f\}$

(ii) $\operatorname{dom} S = 2\mathbb{Z} = \mathbb{E}$; $\operatorname{ran} S = \{2t + 1 \mid t \in \mathbb{Z}\} = \mathbb{O}$; field $S = \mathbb{Z}$

LEVEL 3

5. Let A, B, C, and D be sets with $A \subseteq B$ and $C \subseteq D$. Prove that $A \times C \subseteq B \times D$.

Proof: Let A, B, C, and D be sets with $A \subseteq B$ and $C \subseteq D$, and let $(x, y) \in A \times C$. Then $x \in A$ and $y \in C$. Since $x \in A$ and $A \subseteq B$, $x \in B$. Since $y \in C$ and $C \subseteq D$, $y \in D$. Therefore, $(x, y) \in B \times D$. Since $(x, y) \in A \times C$ was arbitrary, $A \times C \subseteq B \times D$.   □

6. Prove that there do not exist sets A and B such that the relation $<$ on $\mathbb{Z}$ is equal to $A \times B$.

Proof: Suppose toward contradiction that $<= A \times B$ for some sets A and B. Since $1 < 2$ and $2 < 3$, we have $(1, 2), (2, 3) \in A \times B$. Since $(2, 3) \in A \times B$, $2 \in A$. Since $(1, 2) \in A \times B$, $2 \in B$. Therefore, $(2, 2) \in A \times B$. Since $<= A \times B$, $2 < 2$, contradicting that $<$ is antireflexive. Therefore, there do not exist sets A and B such that $<$ is equal to $A \times B$.   □

LEVEL 4

7. Let A, B, C, and D be sets. Determine if each of the following statements is true or false. If true, provide a proof. If false, provide a counterexample.

    (i) $(A \times B) \cap (C \times D) = (A \cap C) \times (B \cap D)$

    (ii) $(A \times B) \cup (C \times D) = (A \cup C) \times (B \cup D)$

Solutions:

(i)   This is **true**.

    Proof: $(x, y) \in (A \times B) \cap (C \times D)$ if and only if $(x, y) \in A \times B$ and $(x, y) \in C \times D$ if and only if $x \in A$, $y \in B$, $x \in C$, and $y \in D$ if and only if $x \in A \cap C$ and $y \in B \cap D$ if and only if $(x, y) \in (A \cap C) \times (B \cap D)$. Therefore, $(A \times B) \cap (C \times D) = (A \cap C) \times (B \cap D)$.   □

23

(ii)   This is **false**. If $A = \{0\}, B = \{1\}, C = \{2\}, D = \{3\}$, then $A \times B = \{(0,1)\}$, $C \times D = \{(2,3)\}$, and so, $(A \times B) \cup (C \times D) = \{(0,1),(2,3)\}$. Also, $A \cup C = \{0,2\}$, $B \cup D = \{1,3\}$, and so, $(A \cup C) \times (B \cup D) = \{(0,1),(0,3),(2,1),(2,3)\}$. Since $(2,1) \in (A \cup C) \times (B \cup D)$, but $(2,1) \notin (A \times B) \cup (C \times D)$, we see that $(A \times B) \cup (C \times D) \neq (A \cup C) \times (B \cup D)$.

8. Prove that $(x,y,z) = (t,u,v)$ if and only if $x = t$, $y = u$, and $z = v$.

Proof: $(x,y,z) = (t,u,v)$ if and only if $\big((x,y),z\big) = \big((t,u),v\big)$ if and only if $(x,y) = (t,u)$ and $z = v$ if and only if $x = t$, $y = u$, and $z = v$. □

LEVEL 5

9. For $a, b \in \mathbb{N}$, we will say that a divides b, written $a|b$, if there is a natural number k such that $b = ak$. Notice that $|$ is a binary relation on $\mathbb{N}$. Prove that $(\mathbb{N}, |)$ is a partially ordered set, but it is not a linearly ordered set.

Proof: If $a \in \mathbb{N}$ then $a = 1a$, so that $a|a$. Therefore, $|$ is reflexive. If $a|b$ and $b|a$, then there are natural numbers j and k such that $b = ja$ and $a = kb$. If $a = 0$, then $b = j \cdot 0 = 0$, and so, $a = b$. Suppose $a \neq 0$. We have $a = k(ja) = (kj)a$. Thus, $(kj - 1)a = (kj)a - 1a = 0$. So, $kj - 1 = 0$, and therefore, $kj = 1$. So, $k = j = 1$. Thus, $b = ja = 1a = a$. Therefore, $|$ is antisymmetric. If $a|b$ and $b|c$, then there are natural numbers j and k such that $b = ja$ and $c = kb$. Then $c = kb = k(ja) = (kj)a$. Since the product of two natural numbers is a natural number, $kj \in \mathbb{N}$. So, $a|c$. Therefore, $|$ is transitive. Since $|$ is reflexive, antisymmetric, and transitive on $\mathbb{N}$, $(\mathbb{N}, |)$ is a partially ordered set. Since 2 and 3 do not divide each other, $(\mathbb{N}, |)$ is **not** linearly ordered. □

Note: We used many facts about $\mathbb{N}$ in this proof based upon our informal understanding of $\mathbb{N}$. A formal definition of $\mathbb{N}$ will be given in Lesson 5 and many of the facts we've been using here will be proved rigorously throughout the book. For example, we said $j \cdot 0 = 0$. This will follow from the formal definition of the product of natural numbers. We also said $(kj - 1)a = (kj)a - 1a = 0$. This assumes a well-defined notion of subtraction and that multiplication is distributive over subtraction in $\mathbb{N}$. As one more example, we stated that the product of two natural numbers is a natural number. These notions will be given a rigorous treatment in Lesson 8.

10. Let R be a relation on a set A. Determine if each of the following statements is true or false. If true, provide a proof. If false, provide a counterexample.

(i)   If R is symmetric and transitive on A, then R is reflexive on A.

(ii) If R is antisymmetric on A, then R is not symmetric on A.

Solutions:

(i)   This is **false**. Let $A = \{0,1\}$ and $R = \{(0,0)\}$. Then R is symmetric and transitive, but not reflexive (because $(1,1) \notin R$).

(ii) This is **false**. $\emptyset$ is both symmetric and antisymmetric on any set A.

Problem Set 5

LEVEL 1

1. Find all partitions of the three-element set $\{a, b, c\}$ and the four-element set $\{a, b, c, d\}$.

Solution: The partitions of $\{a, b, c\}$ are $\{\{a\}, \{b\}, \{c\}\}$, $\{\{a\}, \{b, c\}\}$, $\{\{b\}, \{a, c\}\}$, $\{\{c\}, \{a, b\}\}$, and $\{\{a, b, c\}\}$.

The partitions of $\{a, b, c, d\}$ are $\{\{a\}, \{b\}, \{c\}, \{d\}\}$, $\{\{a\}, \{b\}, \{c, d\}\}$, $\{\{a\}, \{c\}, \{b, d\}\}$, $\{\{a\}, \{d\}, \{b, c\}\}$, $\{\{b\}, \{c\}, \{a, d\}\}$, $\{\{b\}, \{d\}, \{a, c\}\}$, $\{\{c\}, \{d\}, \{a, b\}\}$, $\{\{a, b\}, \{c, d\}\}$, $\{\{a, c\}, \{b, d\}\}$, $\{\{a, d\}, \{b, c\}\}$, $\{\{a, b, c\}, \{d\}\}$, $\{\{a, b, d\}, \{c\}\}$, $\{\{a, c, d\}, \{b\}\}$, $\{\{b, c, d\}, \{a\}\}$, and $\{\{a, b, c, d\}\}$.

2. Let $A = \{1, 2, 3, 4\}$ and let $R = \{(1, 1), (1, 3), (2, 2), (2, 4), (3, 1), (3, 3), (4, 2), (4, 4)\}$. Note that R is an equivalence relation on A. Find the equivalence classes of R.

Solution: The equivalence classes of R are $\{1, 3\}$ and $\{2, 4\}$.

LEVEL 2

3. Prove that for each $n \in \mathbb{Z}^+$, $\equiv_n$ (see part 4 of Example 5.1) is an equivalence relation on $\mathbb{Z}$.

Proof: Let $a \in \mathbb{Z}$. Then $a - a = 0 = n \cdot 0$. So, $n | a - a$. Therefore, $a \equiv_n a$, and so, $\equiv_n$ is reflexive. Let $a, b \in \mathbb{Z}$ and suppose that $a \equiv_n b$. Then $n | b - a$. So, there is $k \in \mathbb{Z}$ such that $b - a = nk$. Thus, $a - b = -(b - a) = -nk = n(-k)$. Since $k \in \mathbb{Z}$, $-k \in \mathbb{Z}$. So, $n | a - b$, and therefore, $b \equiv_n a$. So, $\equiv_n$ is symmetric. Let $a, b, c \in \mathbb{Z}$ with $a \equiv_n b$ and $b \equiv_n c$. Then $n | b - a$ and $n | c - b$. So, there are $j, k \in \mathbb{Z}$ such that $b - a = nj$ and $c - b = nk$. So, $c - a = (c - b) + (b - a) = nk + nj = n(k + j)$. Since $\mathbb{Z}$ is closed under addition, $k + j \in \mathbb{Z}$. Therefore, $n | c - a$. So, $a \equiv_n c$. Thus, $\equiv_n$ is transitive. Since $\equiv_n$ is reflexive, symmetric, and transitive, $\equiv_n$ is an equivalence relation on $\mathbb{Z}$. $\square$

4. Prove that $R = \{((a, b), (c, d)) \in (\mathbb{N} \times \mathbb{N})^2 \mid a + d = b + c\}$ is an equivalence relation on $\mathbb{N} \times \mathbb{N}$.

Proof: Let $(a, b) \in \mathbb{N} \times \mathbb{N}$. Then $a, b \in \mathbb{N}$, and so, $a + b = b + a$. Therefore, $(a, b)R(a, b)$, and so, R is reflexive. Let $(a, b), (c, d) \in \mathbb{N} \times \mathbb{N}$ and suppose that $(a, b)R(c, d)$. Then $a + d = b + c$. It follows that $c + b = d + a$. Therefore, $(c, d)R(a, b)$, and so, R is symmetric. Let $(a, b), (c, d), (e, f) \in \mathbb{N} \times \mathbb{N}$ and suppose that $(a, b)R(c, d)$ and $(c, d)R(e, f)$. Then $a + d = b + c$ and $c + f = d + e$. So, we have $a + c + d + f = b + c + d + e$. Thus, $a + f = b + e$. Therefore, $(a, b)R(e, f)$, and so, R is transitive. Since R is reflexive, symmetric, and transitive, R is an equivalence relation. $\square$

LEVEL 3

5. Prove that $<_{\mathbb{Z}}$ is a well-defined strict linear ordering on $\mathbb{Z}$. You may use the fact that $<_{\mathbb{N}}$ is a well-defined strict linear ordering on $\mathbb{N}$ that is compatible with addition.

Proof: We first show that $<_{\mathbb{Z}}$ is well-defined. Suppose that $(a,b) \sim (a',b')$ and $(c,d) \sim (c',d)$. Since $(a,b) \sim (a',b')$, $a + b' = b + a'$. Since $(c,d) \sim (c',d')$, $c + d' = d + c'$.

We need to check that $[(a,b)] <_{\mathbb{Z}} [(c,d)]$ if and only if $[(a',b')] <_{\mathbb{Z}} [(c',d')]$. We have

$[(a,b)] <_{\mathbb{Z}} [(c,d)]$ if and only if $a + d <_{\mathbb{N}} b + c$ if and only if $a + d + b' + c' <_{\mathbb{N}} b + c + b' + c'$ if and only if $a + b' + d + c' <_{\mathbb{N}} b + c + b' + c'$ if and only if $b + a' + c + d' <_{\mathbb{N}} b + c + b' + c'$ if and only if $b + c + a' + d' <_{\mathbb{N}} b + c + b' + c'$ if and only if $a' + d' < b' + c'$ if and only if $[(a',b')] <_{\mathbb{Z}} [(c',d')]$, as desired.

Next, we show that $<_{\mathbb{Z}}$ is antireflexive. To see this, note that $a + b \not<_{\mathbb{N}} a + b$ because $\not<_{\mathbb{N}}$ is antireflexive. So, $a + b \not<_{\mathbb{N}} b + a$. Therefore, $[(a,b)] \not<_{\mathbb{Z}} [(a,b)]$.

To see that $<_{\mathbb{Z}}$ is antisymmetric, suppose that $[(a,b)] <_{\mathbb{Z}} [(c,d)]$ and $[(c,d)] <_{\mathbb{Z}} [(a,b)]$. Then we have $a + d <_{\mathbb{N}} b + c$ and $c + b <_{\mathbb{N}} d + a$, or equivalently, $b + c <_{\mathbb{N}} a + d$. This is impossible, and so, it is vacuously true that $<_{\mathbb{Z}}$ is antisymmetric.

To see that $<_{\mathbb{Z}}$ is transitive, suppose that $[(a,b)] <_{\mathbb{Z}} [(c,d)]$ and $[(c,d)] <_{\mathbb{Z}} [(e,f)]$. Then we have $a + d <_{\mathbb{N}} b + c$ and $c + f <_{\mathbb{N}} d + e$. By adding each side of these two inequalities we get the inequality $a + d + c + f <_{\mathbb{N}} b + c + d + e$. Cancelling c and d from each side of this last inequality yields $a + f <_{\mathbb{N}} b + e$. Therefore, $[(a,b)] <_{\mathbb{Z}} [(e,f)]$.

Finally, we check that trichotomy holds. Suppose $[(a,b)] \not<_{\mathbb{Z}} [(c,d)]$ and $[(a,b)] \neq [(c,d)]$. Then $a + d \not<_{\mathbb{N}} b + c$ and $a + d \neq b + c$. Since trichotomy holds for $<_{\mathbb{N}}$, we have $b + c <_{\mathbb{N}} a + d$, or equivalently, $c + b <_{\mathbb{N}} d + a$. Therefore, $[(c,d)] <_{\mathbb{Z}} [(a,b)]$. □

> 6. Let X be a set of equivalence relations on a nonempty set A. Prove that $\cap X$ is an equivalence relation on A.

Proof: Let X be a set of equivalence relations on a nonempty set A. Let $x \in A$ and let $R \in X$. Since R is reflexive, $(x,x) \in R$. Since $R \in X$ was arbitrary, $\forall R \in X\big((x,x) \in R\big)$. So, $(x,x) \in \cap X$. Since $x \in A$ was arbitrary, $\cap X$ is reflexive.

Let $(x,y) \in \cap X$ and let $R \in X$. Then $(x,y) \in R$. Since R is an equivalence relation, R is symmetric. Therefore, $(y,x) \in R$. Since $R \in X$ was arbitrary, $\forall R \in X\big((y,x) \in R\big)$. So, $(y,x) \in \cap X$. Since $(x,y) \in \cap X$ was arbitrary, $\cap X$ is symmetric.

Let $(x,y), (y,z) \in \cap X$ and let $R \in X$. Then $(x,y), (y,z) \in R$. Since R is an equivalence relation, R is transitive. Therefore, $(x,z) \in R$. Since $R \in X$ was arbitrary, $\forall R \in X\big((x,z) \in R\big)$. So, $(x,z) \in \cap X$. Since $(x,y), (y,z) \in \cap X$ was arbitrary, $\cap X$ is transitive.

Since $\cap X$ is reflexive, symmetric, and transitive, $\cap X$ is an equivalence relation. □

LEVEL 4

> 7. Prove that addition of integers is well-defined.

26

Proof: Suppose that $(a, b) \sim (a', b')$ and $(c, d) \sim (c', d)$. Since $(a, b) \sim (a', b')$, $a + b' = b + a'$. Since $(c, d) \sim (c', d')$, $c + d' = d + c'$.

We need to check that $(a + c, b + d) \sim (a' + c', b' + d')$, or equivalently, we need to check that $(a + c) + (b' + d') = (b + d) + (a' + c')$

Since $a + b' = b + a'$ and $c + d' = d + c'$, we have

$$(a + c) + (b' + d') = (a + b') + (c + d') = (b + a') + (d + c') = (b + d) + (a' + c').$$

Therefore, $(a + c, b + d) = (a' + c', b' + d')$, as desired.

---

8. Prove that addition and multiplication of rational numbers are well-defined.

Proof: Suppose that $\frac{a}{b} = \frac{a'}{b'}$ and $\frac{c}{d} = \frac{c'}{d'}$. Since $\frac{a}{b} = \frac{a'}{b'}$, we have $ab' = ba'$. Since $\frac{c}{d} = \frac{c'}{d'}$, we have $cd' = dc'$.

We first need to check that $\frac{a}{b} + \frac{c}{d} = \frac{a'}{b'} + \frac{c'}{d'}$, or equivalently, $\frac{ad+bc}{bd} = \frac{a'd'+b'c'}{b'd'}$.

Since $ab' = ba'$ and $cd' = dc'$, we have

$$(ad + bc)(b'd') = adb'd' + bcb'd' = ab'dd' + cd'bb' = ba'dd' + dc'bb'$$
$$= bda'd' + bdb'c' = (bd)(a'd' + b'c').$$

Therefore, $\frac{ad+bc}{bd} = \frac{a'd'+b'c'}{b'd'}$, as desired.

We next need to check that $\frac{a}{b} \cdot \frac{c}{d} = \frac{a'}{b'} \cdot \frac{c'}{d'}$, or equivalently, $\frac{ac}{bd} = \frac{a'c'}{b'd'}$.

Since $ab' = ba'$ and $cd' = dc'$, we have

$$(ac)(b'd') = (ab')(cd') = (ba')(dc') = (bd)(a'c')$$

Therefore, $\frac{ac}{bd} = \frac{a'c'}{b'd'}$, as desired. □

LEVEL 5

9. Let P be a partition of a set S. Prove that there is an equivalence relation $\sim$ on S for which the elements of P are the equivalence classes of $\sim$.

Proof: Let P be a partition of S, and define the relation $\sim$ by $x \sim y$ if and only if there is $X \in P$ with $x, y \in X$.

Let $x \in S$. Since P is a partition of S, $S = \bigcup P$. So, there is $X \in P$ with $x \in X$. It follows that $x \sim x$. Therefore, $\sim$ is reflexive.

If $x \sim y$, then there is $X \in P$ with $x, y \in X$. So, $y, x \in X$ (obviously!). Thus, $y \sim x$, and therefore, $\sim$ is symmetric.

If $x \sim y$ and $y \sim z$, then there are $X, Y \in P$ with $x, y \in X$ and $y, z \in Y$. Since $y \in X$ and $y \in Y$, we have $y \in X \cap Y$. Since P is a partition and $X \cap Y \neq \emptyset$, we must have $X = Y$. So, $z \in X$. Thus, $x, z \in X$, and therefore, $x \sim z$. So, $\sim$ is transitive.

Since $\sim$ is reflexive, symmetric, and transitive on S, $\sim$ is an equivalence relation on S.

We still need to show that $P = \{[x] \mid x \in S\}$. Let $X \in P$ and let $x \in X$. We show that $X = [x]$. Let $y \in X$. Since $x, y \in X$, $x \sim y$. So $y \in [x]$. Thus, $X \subseteq [x]$. Now, let $y \in [x]$. Then $x \sim y$. So, there is $Y \in P$ such that $x, y \in Y$. Since $x \in X$ and $x \in Y$, $x \in X \cap Y$. Since P is a partition and $X \cap Y \neq \emptyset$, we must have $X = Y$. So, $y \in X$. Thus, $[x] \subseteq X$. Since $X \subseteq [x]$ and $[x] \subseteq X$, we have $X = [x]$. Since $X \in P$ was arbitrary, we have shown $P \subseteq \{[x] \mid x \in S\}$.

Now, let $X \in \{[x] \mid x \in S\}$. Then there is $x \in S$ such that $X = [x]$. Since P is a partition of S, $S = \cup P$. So, there is $Y \in P$ with $x \in Y$. We will show that $X = Y$. Let $y \in X$. Then $x \sim y$. So, there is $Z \in P$ with $x, y \in Z$. Since $x \in Y$ and $x \in Z$, $x \in Y \cap Z$. Since P is a partition and $Y \cap Z \neq \emptyset$, we must have $Y = Z$. So, $y \in Y$. Since $y \in X$ was arbitrary, $X \subseteq Y$. Now, let $y \in Y$. Then $x \sim y$. So, $y \in [x] = X$. Since $y \in Y$ was arbitrary, $Y \subseteq X$. Since $X \subseteq Y$ and $Y \subseteq X$, we have $X = Y$. Therefore, $X \in P$. Since $X \in \{[x] \mid x \in S\}$ was arbitrary, we have $\{[x] \mid x \in S\} \subseteq P$.

Since $P \subseteq \{[x] \mid x \in S\}$ and $\{[x] \mid x \in S\} \subseteq P$, we have $P = \{[x] \mid x \in S\}$, as desired. $\qquad \square$

10. Let $\sim$ be an equivalence relation on a set S. Prove that the equivalence classes of $\sim$ form a partition of S.

Proof: Let $\sim$ be an equivalence relation on S. We first show that $\cup\{[x] \mid x \in S\} = S$.

Let $y \in \cup\{[x] \mid x \in S\}$. Then there is $x \in S$ with $y \in [x]$. By definition of $[x]$, $y \in S$. Therefore, $\cup\{[x] \mid x \in S\} \subseteq S$.

Now, let $y \in S$. Since $\sim$ is an equivalence relation, $y \sim y$. So, $y \in [y]$. Thus, $y \in \cup\{[x] \mid x \in S\}$. So, we have $S \subseteq \cup\{[x] \mid x \in S\}$.

Since $\cup\{[x] \mid x \in S\} \subseteq S$ and $S \subseteq \cup\{[x] \mid x \in S\}$, $\cup\{[x] \mid x \in S\} = S$.

We next show that if $x, y \in S$, then $[x] \cap [y] = \emptyset$ or $[x] = [y]$.

Suppose $[x] \cap [y] \neq \emptyset$ and let $z \in [x] \cap [y]$. Then $x \sim z$ and $y \sim z$. Since $\sim$ is symmetric, $z \sim y$. Since $\sim$ is transitive, $x \sim y$. Let $w \in [x]$. Then $x \sim w$. By symmetry, $y \sim x$. By transitivity, $y \sim w$. So, $w \in [y]$. Since $w \in [x]$ was arbitrary, $[x] \subseteq [y]$. By a symmetric argument, $[y] \subseteq [x]$.

Since $[x] \subseteq [y]$ and $[y] \subseteq [x]$, we have $[x] = [y]$.

Since $\cup\{[x] \mid x \in S\} = S$ and every pair of equivalence classes are either disjoint or equal, the set of equivalence classes partitions S. $\qquad \square$

Problem Set 6

LEVEL 1

1. Determine if each of the following relations are functions. For each such function, determine if it is injective. State the domain and range of each function.

   (i) $R = \{(a,b),(b,b),(c,d),(e,a)\}$

   (ii) $S = \{(a,a),(a,b),(b,a)\}$

   (iii) $T = \{(a,b) \mid a,b \in \mathbb{R} \wedge b < 0 \wedge a^2 + b^2 = 9\}$

Solutions:

   (i) R is a function. It is **not** injective. dom $R = \{a,b,c,e\}$ and ran $R = \{a,b,d\}$.

   (ii) S **is not** a function.

   (iii) T is a function. It is **not** injective. dom $T = (-3,3)$ and ran $T = (-3,0)$.

2. Define $f: \mathbb{Z} \to \mathbb{Z}$ by $f(n) = n^2$. Let $A = \{0,1,2,3,4\}$, $B = \mathbb{N}$, and $C = \{-2n \mid n \in \mathbb{N}\}$. Evaluate each of the following:

   (i) $f[A]$

   (ii) $f^{-1}[A]$

   (iii) $f^{-1}[B]$

   (iv) $f^{-1}[B \cup C]$

Solutions:

   (i) $f[A] = \{0,1,4,9,16\}$.

   (ii) $f^{-1}[A] = \{-2,-1,0,1,2\}$.

   (iii) $f^{-1}[B] = \mathbb{Z}$.

   (iv) $f^{-1}[B \cup C] = \mathbb{Z}$.

LEVEL 2

3. Find sets A and B and a function f such that $f[A \cap B] \neq f[A] \cap f[B]$.

Solution: Define $f: \{a,b\} \to \{0\}$ by $\{(a,0),(b,0)\}$. Let $A = \{a\}$ and $B = \{b\}$. Then $A \cap B = \emptyset$. Therefore, $f[A \cap B] = \emptyset$ and $f[A] \cap f[B] = \{0\} \cap \{0\} = \{0\}$.

4. Determine if each of the following sequences are Cauchy sequences. Are any of the Cauchy sequences equivalent?

   (i) $(x_n) = \left(1 + \dfrac{1}{n+1}\right)$

   (ii) $(y_n) = (2^n)$

   (iii) $(z_n) = \left(1 - \dfrac{1}{2n+1}\right)$

Solutions:

   (i)   **Cauchy**

   (ii) **Not Cauchy**

   (iii) **Cauchy**

(x_n) and (z_n) are equivalent.

LEVEL 3

5. For $f, g \in {}^{\mathbb{R}}\mathbb{R}$, define $f \preccurlyeq g$ if and only if for all $x \in \mathbb{R}$, $f(x) \leq g(x)$. Is $({}^{\mathbb{R}}\mathbb{R}, \preccurlyeq)$ a poset? Is it a linearly ordered set? What if we replace $\preccurlyeq$ by $\preccurlyeq^*$, where $f \preccurlyeq^* g$ if and only if there is an $x \in \mathbb{R}$ such that $f(x) \leq g(x)$?

Solution: If $f \in {}^{\mathbb{R}}\mathbb{R}$, then for all $x \in \mathbb{R}$, $f(x) = f(x)$. So, $f \preccurlyeq f$, and therefore, $\preccurlyeq$ is reflexive.

Let $f, g \in {}^{\mathbb{R}}\mathbb{R}$ with $f \preccurlyeq g$ and $g \preccurlyeq f$. Then for all $x \in \mathbb{R}$, $f(x) \leq g(x)$ and $g(x) \leq f(x)$. So, $f = g$, and therefore, $\preccurlyeq$ is antisymmetric.

Let $f, g, h \in {}^{\mathbb{R}}\mathbb{R}$ with $f \preccurlyeq g$ and $g \preccurlyeq h$. Then for all $x \in \mathbb{R}$, $f(x) \leq g(x)$ and $g(x) \leq h(x)$. So, by the transitivity of $\leq$, for all $x \in \mathbb{R}$, $f(x) \leq h(x)$. Thus, $f \preccurlyeq h$, and therefore, $\preccurlyeq$ is transitive.

Since $\preccurlyeq$ is reflexive, antisymmetric, and transitive, $({}^{\mathbb{R}}\mathbb{R}, \preccurlyeq)$ is a poset.

Let $f(x) = x$ and $g(x) = x^2$. Then $f(2) = 2$ and $g(2) = 4$. So, $f(2) < g(2)$. Therefore, $g \not\preccurlyeq f$. We also have $f\left(\frac{1}{2}\right) = \frac{1}{2}$ and $g\left(\frac{1}{2}\right) = \frac{1}{4}$. So, $g\left(\frac{1}{2}\right) < f\left(\frac{1}{2}\right)$. Therefore, $f \not\preccurlyeq g$. So, f and g are incomparible with respect to $\preccurlyeq$. Therefore, $({}^{\mathbb{R}}\mathbb{R}, \preccurlyeq)$ is **not** a linearly ordered set.

The same example from the last paragraph gives us $f \preccurlyeq^* g$ and $g \preccurlyeq^* f$. But $f \neq g$. So, $\preccurlyeq^*$ is **not** antisymmetric, and therefore, $({}^{\mathbb{R}}\mathbb{R}, \preccurlyeq^*)$ is **not** a poset.

6. Prove that the function $f: \mathbb{N} \to \mathbb{Z}$ defined by $f(n) = \begin{cases} \dfrac{n}{2} & \text{if } n \text{ is even} \\ -\dfrac{n+1}{2} & \text{if } n \text{ is odd} \end{cases}$ is a bijection.

Proof: First note that if n is even, then there is $k \in \mathbb{Z}$ with $n = 2k$, and so, $\frac{n}{2} = \frac{2k}{2} = k \in \mathbb{Z}$, and if n is odd, there is $k \in \mathbb{Z}$ with $n = 2k + 1$, and so, $-\frac{n+1}{2} = -\frac{(2k+1)+1}{2} = -\frac{2k+2}{2} = -\frac{2(k+1)}{2} = -(k + 1) \in \mathbb{Z}$. So, f does take each natural number to an integer.

Now, suppose that $n, m \in \mathbb{N}$ with $f(n) = f(m)$. If n and m are both even, we have $\frac{n}{2} = \frac{m}{2}$, and so, $2 \cdot \frac{n}{2} = 2 \cdot \frac{m}{2}$. Thus, $n = m$. If n and m are both odd, we have $-\frac{n+1}{2} = -\frac{m+1}{2}$, and so, $\frac{n+1}{2} = \frac{m+1}{2}$. Thus, $2 \cdot \frac{n+1}{2} = 2 \cdot \frac{m+1}{2}$. So, $n + 1 = m + 1$, and therefore, $n = m$. If n is even and m is odd, then we have $\frac{n}{2} = -\frac{m+1}{2}$. So, $2 \cdot \frac{n}{2} = 2\left(-\frac{m+1}{2}\right)$. Therefore, $n = -(m + 1)$. Since $m \in \mathbb{N}$, $m \geq 0$. So, $m + 1 \geq 1$. Therefore, $n = -(m + 1) \leq -1$, contradicting $n \in \mathbb{N}$. So, it is impossible for n to be even, m to be odd, and $f(n) = f(m)$. Similarly, we cannot have n odd and m even. So, f is an injection.

Now, let $k \in \mathbb{Z}$. If $k \geq 0$, then $2k \in \mathbb{N}$ and $f(2k) = \frac{2k}{2} = k$. If $k < 0$, then $-2k > 0$, and so, we have $-2k - 1 \in \mathbb{N}$. Then $f(-2k - 1) = -\frac{(-2k-1)+1}{2} = -\frac{-2k}{2} = k$. So, f is a surjection.

Since f is both an injection and a surjection, f is a bijection. $\qquad\square$

LEVEL 4

7. For $f, g \in {}^{\mathbb{N}}\mathbb{N}$, define $f <^* g$ if and only if there is $n \in \mathbb{N}$ such that for all $m > n$, $f(m) < g(m)$.

   (i)   Is $({}^{\mathbb{N}}\mathbb{N}, <^*)$ a strict poset?

   (ii) Is $({}^{\mathbb{N}}\mathbb{N}, <^*)$ a strict linearly ordered set?

   (iii) Let $\mathcal{F} = \{f_n : \mathbb{N} \to \mathbb{N} \mid n \in \mathbb{N}\}$ be a set of functions. Must there be a function $g \in {}^{\mathbb{N}}\mathbb{N}$ such that for all $n \in \mathbb{N}$, $f_n <^* g$?

Solutions:

(i) If $f \in {}^{\mathbb{N}}\mathbb{N}$, then for all $n \in \mathbb{N}$, $f(n) = f(n)$. So, $f \not<^* f$, and therefore, $<^*$ is antireflexive.

Let $f, g \in {}^{\mathbb{N}}\mathbb{N}$ with $f <^* g$ and $g <^* f$. Since $f <^* g$, there is $n_1 \in \mathbb{N}$ such that for all $m > n_1$, $f(m) < g(m)$. Since $g <^* f$, there is $n_2 \in \mathbb{N}$ such that for all $m > n_2$, $g(m) < f(m)$. Let $n = \max\{n_1, n_2\}$. Then $f(n + 1) < g(n + 1)$ and $g(n + 1) < f(n + 1)$. By the transitivity of $<$, we have $f(n + 1) < f(n + 1)$, a contradiction. So, antisymmetry holds (vacuously).

Let $f, g, h \in {}^{\mathbb{N}}\mathbb{N}$ with $f <^* g$ and $g <^* h$. Since $f <^* g$, there is $n_1 \in \mathbb{N}$ such that for all $m > n_1$, $f(m) < g(m)$. Since $g <^* h$, there is $n_2 \in \mathbb{N}$ such that for all $m > n_2$, $g(m) < h(m)$. Let $n = \max\{n_1, n_2\}$. Then for $m > n$, we have $f(m) < g(m)$ and $g(m) < h(m)$. By the transitivity of $<$, for $m > n$, we have $f(m) < h(m)$. So, $f <^* h$. Therefore, $<^*$ is transitive.

Since $<^*$ is antireflexive, antisymmetric, and transitive, $({}^{\mathbb{N}}\mathbb{N}, <^*)$ is a strict poset.

31

(ii)   Let $f(n) = \frac{1}{2}$ and $g(n) = \begin{cases} 0 & \text{if } n \text{ is even} \\ 1 & \text{if } n \text{ is odd} \end{cases}$. Then for each $k \in \mathbb{N}$, $g(2k) = 0 < \frac{1}{2} = f(2k)$.
So, $f \not<^* g$. Also, for each $k \in \mathbb{N}$, $g(2k+1) = 1 > \frac{1}{2} = f(2k+1)$. Therefore, $g \not<^* f$. So, f and g are incomparible with respect to $<^*$. Therefore, $({}^{\mathbb{N}}\mathbb{N}, <^*)$ is **not** a strict linearly ordered set.

(iii)   Let $\mathcal{F} = \{f_n \colon \mathbb{N} \to \mathbb{N} \mid n \in \mathbb{N}\}$ and define $g \colon \mathbb{N} \to \mathbb{N}$ by $g(k) = \max\{f_n(k) + 1 \mid n \leq k\}$.

Let $n \in \mathbb{N}$. If $m > n$, then we have $f_n(m) < f_n(m) + 1 \leq g(m)$. So, $f_n <^* g$. It follows that for all $n \in \mathbb{N}$, $f_n <^* g$.

Notes: (1) To better understand the definition of $<^*$, let's look at an example. Define $f, g \colon \mathbb{N} \to \mathbb{N}$ by $f(n) = n + 100$ and $g(n) = 2^n$. Observe that $f(m) < g(m)$ for $m > 6$. It follows that $f <^* g$.

Note that $f(1) = 101$ and $g(1) = 2^1 = 2$, so that $f(1) > g(1)$. So, it's not true that $f(n) < g(n)$ for all n. The definition of $<^*$ allows for this. $f <^* g$ means that the values of f are *eventually* less than the values of g. The expression $f <^* g$ is usually read as "f is **dominated** by g" or "g **dominates** f."

(2) Consider the family $\mathcal{F} = \{f_n \colon \mathbb{N} \to \mathbb{N} \mid n \in \mathbb{N}\}$, where $f_n(k) = n$ for all $k \in \mathbb{N}$. For each $n \in \mathbb{N}$, f_n is a constant function. For example, f_0 is the function which gives an output of 0 for each natural number input. You can visualize this constant function as dots along the x-axis, as shown in the figure to the right. The figure also shows the functions f_1, f_2, and f_3. There is no function g such that for all $n \in \mathbb{N}$, $f_n(k) < g(k)$ for all $k \in \mathbb{N}$. However, there are functions which dominate every f_n. For example, let $g \colon \mathbb{N} \to \mathbb{N}$ be defined by $g(n) = n$. You can visualize g as the dots along the diagonal ray shown in the figure to the right. We see that $f_0(k) < g(k)$ for all $k > 0$. We also see that $f_1(k) < g(k)$ for all $k > 1$. In general, $f_n(k) < g(k)$ for all $k > n$.

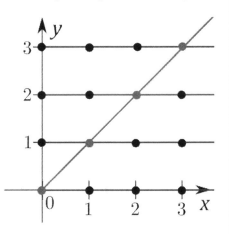

8.   Let $A = \{(x_n) \mid (x_n) \text{ is a Cauchy sequence of rational numbers}\}$ and define the relation R on A by $(x_n)R(y_n)$ if and only for every $k \in \mathbb{N}^+$, there is $K \in \mathbb{N}$ such that $n > K$ implies $|x_n - y_n| < \frac{1}{k}$. Prove that R is an equivalence relation on A.

Proof: Let $(x_n) \in A$, let $k \in \mathbb{N}^+$ and let $K = 0$. Then $n > K$ implies $|x_n - x_n| = 0 < \frac{1}{k}$. So, $(x_n)R(x_n)$, and therefore, R is reflexive.

Since $|x_n - y_n| = |y_n - x_n|$, it is clear that R is symmetric.

Let $(x_n), (y_n), (z_n) \in A$ with $(x_n)R(y_n)$ and $(y_n)R(z_n)$ and let $k \in \mathbb{N}^+$. Since $(x_n)R(y_n)$, there is $K_1 \in \mathbb{N}$ such that $n > K_1$ implies $|x_n - y_n| < \frac{1}{2k}$. Since $(y_n)R(z_n)$, there is $K_2 \in \mathbb{N}$ such that $n > K_2$ implies $|y_n - z_n| < \frac{1}{2k}$. Let $K = \max\{K_1, K_2\}$. Let $n > K$. Since $K \geq K_1$, $n > K_1$, and therefore, we have $|x_n - y_n| < \frac{1}{2k}$. Since $K \geq K_2$, $n > K_2$, and therefore, we have $|y_n - z_n| < \frac{1}{2k}$. It follows that

$$|x_n - z_n| = |x_n - y_n + y_n - z_n| \le |x_n - y_n| + |y_n - z_n| < \frac{1}{2k} + \frac{1}{2k} = 2 \cdot \frac{1}{2k} = \frac{1}{k}.$$

So, $(x_n)R(z_n)$, and therefore, R is transitive.

Since R is reflexive, symmetric, and transitive, it follows that R is an equivalence relation. $\square$

LEVEL 5

9. Let X be a nonempty set of sets and let f be a function such that $\bigcup X \subseteq \operatorname{dom} f$. Prove each of the following:

    (i) $f[\bigcup X] = \bigcup\{f[A] \mid A \in X\}$
    (ii) $f[\bigcap X] \subseteq \bigcap\{f[A] \mid A \in X\}$
    (iii) $f^{-1}[\bigcup X] = \bigcup\{f^{-1}[A] \mid A \in X\}$
    (iv) $f^{-1}[\bigcap X] = \bigcap\{f^{-1}[A] \mid A \in X\}$

Proofs:

(i)   Let $y \in f[\bigcup X]$. Then there is $x \in \bigcup X$ such that $f(x) = y$. Since $x \in \bigcup X$, there is $B \in X$ such that $x \in B$. So, $y = f(x) \in f[B]$. Therefore, $y \in \bigcup\{f[A] \mid A \in X\}$. Since $y \in f[\bigcup X]$ was arbitrary, we see that $f[\bigcup X] \subseteq \bigcup\{f[A] \mid A \in X\}$.

Now, let $y \in \bigcup\{f[A] \mid A \in X\}$. Then there is $B \in X$ such that $y \in f[B]$. So, there is $x \in B$ such that $y = f(x)$. By Problem 9 (part (i)) from Problem Set 3, $B \subseteq \bigcup X$. Since $x \in B$ and $B \subseteq \bigcup X, x \in \bigcup X$. Thus, $y = f(x) \in f[\bigcup X]$. Since $y \in \bigcup\{f[A] \mid A \in X\}$ was arbitrary, we see that $\bigcup\{f[A] \mid A \in X\} \subseteq f[\bigcup X]$.

Since $f[\bigcup X] \subseteq \bigcup\{f[A] \mid A \in X\}$ and $\bigcup\{f[A] \mid A \in X\} \subseteq f[\bigcup X]$, it follows that $f[\bigcup X] = \bigcup\{f[A] \mid A \in X\}$. $\square$

(ii) Let $y \in f[\bigcap X]$. Then there is $x \in \bigcap X$ such that $f(x) = y$. Let $B \in X$. Since $x \in \bigcap X, x \in B$. So, $y = f(x) \in f[B]$. Since $B \in X$ was arbitrary, $y \in \bigcap\{f[A] \mid A \in X\}$. Since $y \in f[\bigcap X]$ was arbitrary, we see that $f[\bigcap X] \subseteq \bigcap\{f[A] \mid A \in X\}$. $\square$

(iii) $x \in f^{-1}[\bigcup X]$ if and only if $f(x) \in \bigcup X$ if and only if there is $A \in X$ such that $f(x) \in A$ if and only if there is $A \in X$ such that $x \in f^{-1}[A]$ if and only if $x \in \bigcup\{f^{-1}[A] \mid A \in X\}$. Therefore, $f^{-1}[\bigcup X] = \bigcup\{f^{-1}[A] \mid A \in X\}$. $\square$

(iv) $x \in f^{-1}[\bigcap X]$ if and only if $f(x) \in \bigcap X$ if and only for all $A \in X, f(x) \in A$ if and only if for all $A \in X, x \in f^{-1}[A]$ if and only if $x \in \bigcap\{f^{-1}[A] \mid A \in X\}$. Therefore, we see that $f^{-1}[\bigcap X] = \bigcap\{f^{-1}[A] \mid A \in X\}$. $\square$

10. Prove that addition of real numbers is well-defined and that the sum of two real numbers is a real number.

Proof: Suppose that $[(x_n)] = [(z_n)]$ and $[(y_n)] = [(w_n)]$. To prove that addition is well-defined, we need to show that $[(x_n + y_n)] = [(z_n + w_n)]$.

Let $k \in \mathbb{N}^+$. Since $[(x_n)] = [(z_n)]$, there is $K_1 \in \mathbb{N}$ such that $n > K_1$ implies $|x_n - z_n| < \frac{1}{2k}$. Since $[(y_n)] = [(w_n)]$, there is $K_2 \in \mathbb{N}$ such that $n > K_2$ implies $|y_n - w_n| < \frac{1}{2k}$. Let $K = \max\{K_1, K_2\}$. Let $n > K$. Since $K \geq K_1$, $n > K_1$, and therefore, we have $|x_n - z_n| < \frac{1}{2k}$. Since $K \geq K_2$, $n > K_2$, and therefore, we have $|y_n - w_n| < \frac{1}{2k}$. It follows that

$$|(x_n + y_n) - (z_n + w_n)| = |(x_n - z_n) + (y_n - w_n)| \leq |x_n - z_n| + |y_n - w_n| < \frac{1}{2k} + \frac{1}{2k} = \frac{1}{k}.$$

So, $[(x_n + y_n)] = [(z_n + w_n)]$, as desired.

We now prove that the sum of two real numbers is a real number. Let $[(x_n)]$ and $[(y_n)]$ be real numbers. Since the sum of two rational numbers is a rational number, for each $n \in \mathbb{N}$, we have $x_n + y_n \in \mathbb{Q}$. We need to show that $(x_n + y_n)$ is a Cauchy sequence. To see this, let $k \in \mathbb{N}^+$. Since (x_n) is a Cauchy sequence, there is $K_1 \in \mathbb{N}$ such that $m \geq n > K_1$ implies $|x_m - x_n| < \frac{1}{2k}$. Since (y_n) is a Cauchy sequence, there is $K_2 \in \mathbb{N}$ such that $m \geq n > K_2$ implies $|y_m - y_n| < \frac{1}{2k}$. Let $K = \max\{K_1, K_2\}$ and let $k \in \mathbb{N}^+$. Suppose that $m \geq n > K$. Since $K \geq K_1$, we have $|x_m - x_n| < \frac{1}{2k}$. Since $K \geq K_2$, we have $|y_m - y_n| < \frac{1}{2k}$. So,

$$|(x_m + y_m) - (x_n + y_n)| = |(x_m - x_n) + (y_m - y_n)| \leq |x_m - x_n| + |y_m - y_n| < \frac{1}{2k} + \frac{1}{2k} = \frac{1}{k}.$$

Therefore, $(x_n + y_n)$ is a Cauchy sequence. $\qquad\square$

Problem Set 7

LEVEL 1

> 1. Let A and B be sets such that $A \subseteq B$. Prove that $\mathcal{P}(A) \preccurlyeq \mathcal{P}(B)$.

Proof: Suppose that $A \subseteq B$. We show that $\mathcal{P}(A) \subseteq \mathcal{P}(B)$. Let $X \in \mathcal{P}(A)$. Then $X \subseteq A$. Since $X \subseteq A$ and $A \subseteq B$, and $\subseteq$ is transitive (Theorem 2.3), we have $X \subseteq B$. Therefore, $X \in \mathcal{P}(B)$. Since X was an arbitrary element of $\mathcal{P}(A)$, we have shown that every element of $\mathcal{P}(A)$ is an element of $\mathcal{P}(B)$. Therefore, $\mathcal{P}(A) \subseteq \mathcal{P}(B)$. By Note 1 following Example 7.3, $\mathcal{P}(A) \preccurlyeq \mathcal{P}(B)$. □

> 2. Let A, B, and C be sets. Prove the following:
>   (i) $\preccurlyeq$ is transitive.
>   (ii) $\prec$ is transitive.
>   (iii) If $A \preccurlyeq B$ and $B \prec C$, then $A \prec C$.
>   (iv) If $A \prec B$ and $B \preccurlyeq C$, then $A \prec C$.

Proofs:

(i)   Suppose that $A \preccurlyeq B$ and $B \preccurlyeq C$. Then there are functions $f: A \hookrightarrow B$ and $g: B \hookrightarrow C$. By Theorem 6.1, $g \circ f: A \hookrightarrow C$. So, $A \preccurlyeq C$. Therefore, $\preccurlyeq$ is transitive. □

(ii) Suppose that $A \prec B$ and $B \prec C$. Then $A \preccurlyeq B$ and $B \preccurlyeq C$. By (i), $A \preccurlyeq C$. Assume toward contradiction that $A \sim C$. Since $\sim$ is symmetric, $C \sim A$. In particular, $C \preccurlyeq A$. Since $C \preccurlyeq A$ and $A \preccurlyeq B$, by (i), $C \preccurlyeq B$. Since $B \preccurlyeq C$ and $C \preccurlyeq B$, by the Cantor-Schroeder-Bernstein Theorem, $B \sim C$, contradicting $B \prec C$. It follows that $A \nsim C$, and thus, $A \prec C$. □

(iii) Suppose that $A \preccurlyeq B$ and $B \prec C$. Then $B \preccurlyeq C$. By (i), $A \preccurlyeq C$. Assume toward contradiction that $A \sim C$. The rest of the argument is the same as (ii). □

(iv) Suppose that $A \prec B$ and $B \preccurlyeq C$. Then $A \preccurlyeq B$. By (i), $A \preccurlyeq C$. Assume toward contradiction that $A \sim C$. Since $\sim$ is symmetric, $C \sim A$. In particular, $C \preccurlyeq A$. Since $B \preccurlyeq C$ and $C \preccurlyeq A$, by (i), $B \preccurlyeq A$. Since $A \preccurlyeq B$ and $B \preccurlyeq A$, by the Cantor-Schroeder-Bernstein Theorem, $A \sim B$, contradicting $A \prec B$. It follows that $A \nsim C$, and thus, $A \prec C$. □

LEVEL 2

> 3. Define $\mathcal{P}_k(\mathbb{N})$ for each $k \in \mathbb{N}$ by $\mathcal{P}_0(\mathbb{N}) = \mathbb{N}$ and $\mathcal{P}_{k+1}(\mathbb{N}) = \mathcal{P}\big(\mathcal{P}_k(\mathbb{N})\big)$ for $k > 0$. Find a set B such that for all $k \in \mathbb{N}$, $\mathcal{P}_k(\mathbb{N}) \prec B$.

Solution: Let $B = \bigcup \{\mathcal{P}_n(\mathbb{N}) \mid n \in \mathbb{N}\}$. Let $k \in \mathbb{N}$. Since $\mathcal{P}_k(\mathbb{N}) \subseteq B$, by Note 1 following Example 7.3, $\mathcal{P}_k(\mathbb{N}) \preccurlyeq B$. Since k was arbitrary, we have $\mathcal{P}_k(\mathbb{N}) \preccurlyeq B$ for all $k \in \mathbb{N}$. Again, let $k \in \mathbb{N}$. We have $\mathcal{P}_k(\mathbb{N}) \prec \mathcal{P}_{k+1}(\mathbb{N})$ and $\mathcal{P}_{k+1}(\mathbb{N}) \preccurlyeq B$. By Problem 2 (part (iv)), $\mathcal{P}_k(\mathbb{N}) \prec B$. Since $k \in \mathbb{N}$ was arbitrary, we have shown that for all $k \in \mathbb{N}$, $\mathcal{P}_k(\mathbb{N}) \prec B$.

> 4. Prove that if $A \sim B$ and $C \sim D$, then $A \times C \sim B \times D$.

Proof: Suppose that $A \sim B$ and $C \sim D$. Then there exist bijections $h: A \to B$ and $k: C \to D$. Define $f: A \times C \to B \times D$ by $f(a,c) = (h(a), k(c))$.

Suppose $(a,c), (a',c') \in A \times C$ with $f((a,c)) = f((a',c'))$. Then $(h(a), k(c)) = (h(a'), k(c'))$. So, $h(a) = h(a')$ and $k(c) = k(c')$. Since h is an injection, $a = a'$. Since k is an injection, $c = c'$. Since $a = a'$ and $c = c'$, $(a,c) = (a',c')$. Since $(a,c), (a',c') \in A \times C$ were arbitrary, f is an injection.

Now, let $(b,d) \in B \times D$. Since h and k are bijections, h^{-1} and k^{-1} exist. Let $a = h^{-1}(b)$, $c = k^{-1}(d)$. Then $f(a,c) = (h(a), k(c)) = \left(h(h^{-1}(b)), k(k^{-1}(d))\right) = (b,d)$. Since $(b,d) \in B \times D$ was arbitrary, f is a surjection.

Since f is both an injection and a surjection, $A \times C \sim B \times D$. $\qquad\square$

LEVEL 3

5. Prove the following:

    (i) There is a partition P of $\mathbb{N}$ such that $P \sim \mathbb{N}$ and for each $X \in P$, $X \sim \mathbb{N}$

    (ii) A countable union of countable sets is countable.

Proofs:

(i) For each $n \in \mathbb{N}$, let P_n be the set of natural numbers ending with exactly n zeros and let $P = \{P_n \mid n \in \mathbb{N}\}$. For example, $5231 \in P_0$, $0 \in P_1$, and $26{,}200 \in P_2$. Let's define $\widetilde{m,n}$ to be the natural number consisting of m 1's followed by n 0's. For example, $\widetilde{3,0} = 111$ and $\widetilde{2,5} = 1{,}100{,}000$. For each $n \in \mathbb{N}$, $\{\widetilde{m,n} \mid m \in \mathbb{N}\} \subseteq P_n$ showing that each P_n is equinumerous to $\mathbb{N}$. Also, if $k \in P_n \cap P_m$, then k ends with exactly n zeros and exactly m zeros, and so, $n = m$. Therefore, P is pairwise disjoint. This also shows that the function $f: \mathbb{N} \to P$ defined by $f(n) = P_n$ is a bijection. So, $P \sim \mathbb{N}$. Finally, if $k \in \mathbb{N}$, then there is $n \in \mathbb{N}$ such that k ends with exactly n zeros. So, $\bigcup P = \mathbb{N}$. $\qquad\square$

(ii) For each $n \in \mathbb{N}$, let A_n be a countable set. By replacing each A_n by $A_n \times \{n\}$, we can assume that $\{A_n \mid n \in \mathbb{N}\}$ is a pairwise disjoint collection of sets ($A_n \sim A_n \times \{n\}$ via the bijection f sending x to (x,n)). By (i), there is a partition P of $\mathbb{N}$ such that $P \sim \mathbb{N}$ and for each $X \in P$, $X \sim \mathbb{N}$. Let's say $P = \{P_n \mid n \in \mathbb{N}\}$. Since each A_n is countable, for each $n \in \mathbb{N}$ there are injective functions $f_n: A_n \to P_n$. Define $f: \bigcup\{A_n \mid n \in \mathbb{N}\} \to \mathbb{N}$ by $f(x) = f_n(x)$ if $x \in A_n$.

Since $\{A_n \mid n \in \mathbb{N}\}$ is pairwise disjoint, f is well-defined.

Suppose that $x, y \in \bigcup\{A_n \mid n \in \mathbb{N}\}$ with $f(x) = f(y)$. There exist $n, m \in \mathbb{N}$ such that $x \in A_n$ and $y \in A_m$. So, $f(x) = f_n(x) \in P_n$ and $f(y) = f_m(y) \in P_m$. Since $f(x) = f(y)$, we have $f_n(x) = f_m(y)$. Since for $n \neq m$, $P_n \cap P_m = \emptyset$, we must have $n = m$. So, we have $f_n(x) = f_n(y)$. Since f_n is injective, $x = y$. Since $x, y \in \bigcup\{A_n \mid n \in \mathbb{N}\}$ were arbitrary, f is an injective function. Therefore, $\bigcup\{A_n \mid n \in \mathbb{N}\}$ is countable. $\qquad\square$

6. Let A and B be sets such that $A \sim B$. Prove that $\mathcal{P}(A) \sim \mathcal{P}(B)$.

Proof: Suppose that $A \sim B$. Then there exists a bijection $h: A \to B$. Define $F: \mathcal{P}(A) \to \mathcal{P}(B)$ by $F(X) = \{h(a) \mid a \in X\}$ for each $X \in \mathcal{P}(A)$.

Suppose $X, Y \in \mathcal{P}(A)$ with $F(X) = F(Y)$. Let $a \in X$. Then $h(a) \in F(X)$. Since $F(X) = F(Y)$, $h(a) \in F(Y)$. So, there is $b \in Y$ such that $h(a) = h(b)$. Since h is injective, $a = b$. So, $a \in Y$. Since $a \in X$ was arbitrary, $X \subseteq Y$. By a symmetrical argument, $Y \subseteq X$. Therefore, $X = Y$. Since $X, Y \in \mathcal{P}(A)$ were arbitrary, F is injective.

Let $Y \in \mathcal{P}(B)$, and let $X = \{a \in A \mid h(a) \in Y\}$. Then $b \in F(X)$ if and only if $b = h(a)$ for some $a \in X$ if and only if $b \in Y$ (because h is surjective). So, $F(X) = Y$. Since $Y \in \mathcal{P}(B)$ was arbitrary, F is surjective.

Since F is injective and surjective, $\mathcal{P}(A) \sim \mathcal{P}(B)$. $\square$

LEVEL 4

7. Prove the following:

   (i) $\mathbb{N} \times \mathbb{N} \sim \mathbb{N}$.

   (ii) $\mathbb{Q} \sim \mathbb{N}$.

   (iii) Any two intervals of real numbers are equinumerous (including $\mathbb{R}$ itself).

   (iv) $^{\mathbb{N}}\mathbb{N} \sim \mathcal{P}(\mathbb{N})$.

Proofs:

(i) $\mathbb{N} \times \mathbb{N} = \bigcup\{\mathbb{N} \times \{n\} \mid n \in \mathbb{N}\}$. This is a countable union of countable sets. By Problem 5 (part(ii)), $\mathbb{N} \times \mathbb{N}$ is countable. $\square$

(ii) $\mathbb{Q}^{+} = \left\{\frac{a}{b} \mid a \in \mathbb{N} \wedge b \in \mathbb{N}^{+}\right\} = \bigcup\left\{\left\{\frac{a}{b} \mid a \in \mathbb{N}\right\} \mid b \in \mathbb{N}^{+}\right\}$. This is a countable union of countable sets. By Problem 5 (part(ii)), $\mathbb{Q}^{+}$ is countable. Now, $\mathbb{Q} = \mathbb{Q}^{+} \cup \{0\} \cup \mathbb{Q}^{-}$, where $\mathbb{Q}^{-} = \{q \in \mathbb{Q} \mid -q \in \mathbb{Q}^{+}\}$. This is again a countable union of countable sets, thus countable. So, $\mathbb{Q} \sim \mathbb{N}$. $\square$

(iii) The function $f: \mathbb{R} \to (0, \infty)$ defined by $f(x) = 2^{x}$ is a bijection. So, $\mathbb{R} \sim (0, \infty)$. The function $g: (0, \infty) \to (0, 1)$ defined by $g(x) = \frac{1}{x^{2}+1}$ is a bijection. So, $(0, \infty) \sim (0, 1)$. If $a, b \in \mathbb{R}$, the function $h: (0, 1) \to (a, b)$ defined by $h(x) = (b - a)x + a$ is a bijection. So, $(0, 1) \sim (a, b)$. It follows that all bounded open intervals are equinumerous with each other and $\mathbb{R}$.

We have, $[a, b] \subseteq (a - 1, b + 1) \sim (a, b) \subseteq [a, b) \subseteq [a, b]$ and $(a, b) \subseteq (a, b] \subseteq [a, b]$. It follows that all bounded intervals are equinumerous with each other and $\mathbb{R}$.

We also have the following.

$$(a, \infty) \subseteq [a, \infty) \subseteq \mathbb{R} \sim (a, a + 1) \subseteq (a, \infty)$$
$$(-\infty, b) \subseteq (-\infty, b] \subseteq \mathbb{R} \sim (b - 1, b) \subseteq (-\infty, b)$$

Therefore, all unbounded intervals are equinumerous with $\mathbb{R}$. It follows that any two intervals of real numbers are equinumerous. $\square$

(iv) $^\mathbb{N}\mathbb{N} \subseteq \mathcal{P}(\mathbb{N} \times \mathbb{N})$ by the definition of $^\mathbb{N}\mathbb{N}$. So, $^\mathbb{N}\mathbb{N} \preccurlyeq \mathcal{P}(\mathbb{N} \times \mathbb{N})$ by Note 1 following Example 7.3. By (i) above, $\mathbb{N} \times \mathbb{N} \sim \mathbb{N}$. So, by Problem 6, $\mathcal{P}(\mathbb{N} \times \mathbb{N}) \sim \mathcal{P}(\mathbb{N})$. Thus, $\mathcal{P}(\mathbb{N} \times \mathbb{N}) \preccurlyeq \mathcal{P}(\mathbb{N})$. Since $\preccurlyeq$ is transitive, $^\mathbb{N}\mathbb{N} \preccurlyeq \mathcal{P}(\mathbb{N})$.

Now, $\mathcal{P}(\mathbb{N}) \sim {}^\mathbb{N}\{0, 1\}$ (see Example 7.1 (part 5)). So, $\mathcal{P}(\mathbb{N}) \preccurlyeq {}^\mathbb{N}\{0, 1\}$. Also, $^\mathbb{N}\{0, 1\} \subseteq {}^\mathbb{N}\mathbb{N}$, and so, by Note 1 following Example 7.3, $^\mathbb{N}\{0, 1\} \preccurlyeq {}^\mathbb{N}\mathbb{N}$. Since $\preccurlyeq$ is transitive, $\mathcal{P}(\mathbb{N}) \preccurlyeq {}^\mathbb{N}\mathbb{N}$.

By the Cantor-Schroeder-Bernstein Theorem, $^\mathbb{N}\mathbb{N} \sim \mathcal{P}(\mathbb{N})$. □

Notes: (1) In the proof of (iii), we used the fact that equinumerosity is an equivalence relation, the Cantor-Schroeder-Bernstein Theorem, and Problem 2 many times without mention. For example, we have $\mathbb{R} \sim (0, \infty)$ and $(0, \infty) \sim (0, 1)$. So, by the transitivity of $\sim$, we have $\mathbb{R} \sim (0, 1)$. As another example, the sequence $(a, \infty) \subseteq [a, \infty) \subseteq \mathbb{R} \sim (a, a + 1) \subseteq (a, \infty)$ together with Note 1 following Example 7.3 gives us that $(a, \infty) \preccurlyeq \mathbb{R}$ and $\mathbb{R} \preccurlyeq (a, \infty)$. By the Cantor-Schroeder-Bernstein Theorem, $(a, \infty) \sim \mathbb{R}$.

(2) Once we showed that for all $a, b \in \mathbb{R}$, $(0, 1) \sim (a, b)$, it follows from the fact that $\sim$ is an equivalence relation that any two bounded open intervals are equinumerous. Indeed, if (a, b) and (c, d) are bounded open intervals, then $(0, 1) \sim (a, b)$ and $(0, 1) \sim (c, d)$. By the symmetry of $\sim$, we have $(a, b) \sim (0, 1)$, and finally, by the transitivity of $\sim$, we have $(a, b) \sim (c, d)$.

(3) It's easy to prove that two specific intervals of real numbers are equinumerous using just the fact that any two bounded open intervals are equinumerous with each other, together with the fact that $\mathbb{R} \sim (0, 1)$. For example, to show that $[3, \infty)$ is equinumerous with $(-2, 5]$, simply consider the following sequence: $[3, \infty) \subseteq \mathbb{R} \sim (0, 1) \sim (-2, 5) \subseteq (-2, 5] \subseteq (-2, 6) \sim (3, 4) \subseteq [3, \infty)$.

> 8. Prove that if $A \sim B$ and $C \sim D$, then $^AC \sim {}^BD$.

Proof: Suppose that $A \sim B$ and $C \sim D$. Then there exist bijections $h : A \to B$ and $k : C \to D$. Define $F : {}^AC \to {}^BD$ by $F(f)(b) = k\left(f\left(h^{-1}(b)\right)\right)$.

Suppose $f, g \in {}^AC$ with $F(f) = F(g)$. Let $a \in A$, and let $b = h(a)$. We have $F(f)(b) = F(g)(b)$, or equivalently, $k\left(f\left(h^{-1}(b)\right)\right) = k\left(g\left(h^{-1}(b)\right)\right)$. Since k is injective, $f\left(h^{-1}(b)\right) = g\left(h^{-1}(b)\right)$. Since $b = h(a)$, $a = h^{-1}(b)$. So, $f(a) = g(a)$. Since $a \in A$ was arbitrary, $f = g$. Since $f, g \in {}^AC$ were arbitrary, F is injective.

Now, let $g \in {}^BD$ and let's define $f \in {}^AC$ by $f(a) = k^{-1}\left(g(h(a))\right)$. Let $b \in B$. Then we have

$$F(f)(b) = k\left(f\left(h^{-1}(b)\right)\right) = k\left(k^{-1}\left(g\left(h\left(h^{-1}(b)\right)\right)\right)\right) = g(b).$$ Since $b \in B$ was arbitrary, we have $F(f) = g$. Since $g \in {}^BD$ was arbitrary, F is surjective.

Since F is injective and surjective, $^AC \sim {}^BD$. □

9. Prove that for any sets A, B, and C, ${}^{B\times C}A \sim {}^{C}({}^{B}A)$.

Proof: Let A, B, and C be sets, and define $F\colon {}^{B\times C}A \to {}^{C}({}^{B}A)$ by $F(f)(c)(b) = f(b,c)$.

Suppose $f, g \in {}^{B\times C}A$ with $F(f) = F(g)$. Let $c \in C$. Since $F(f) = F(g)$, $F(f)(c) = F(g)(c)$. So, for all $b \in B$, $F(f)(c)(b) = F(g)(c)(b)$. So, for all $b \in B$, $f(b,c) = g(b,c)$. Since $c \in C$ was arbitrary, for all $b \in B$ and $c \in C$, $f(b,c) = g(b,c)$. Therefore, $f = g$. Since $f, g \in {}^{B\times C}A$ were arbitrary, F is injective.

Let $k \in {}^{C}({}^{B}A)$ and define $f \in {}^{B\times C}A$ by $f(b,c) = k(c)(b)$. Then $F(f)(c)(b) = f(b,c) = k(c)(b)$. So, $F(f) = k$. Since $k \in {}^{C}({}^{B}A)$ was arbitrary, F is surjective.

Since F is injective and surjective, ${}^{B\times C}A \sim {}^{C}({}^{B}A)$. $\qquad\square$

10. Prove the following:

   (i) $\mathcal{P}(\mathbb{N}) \sim \{f \in {}^{\mathbb{N}}\mathbb{N} \mid f \text{ is a bijection}\}$.

   (ii) $\mathbb{R} \sim \mathcal{P}(\mathbb{N})$.

   (iii) ${}^{\mathbb{N}}\mathbb{R} \nsim {}^{\mathbb{R}}\mathbb{N}$.

Proofs:

(i)   Let $S = \{f \in {}^{\mathbb{N}}\mathbb{N} \mid f \text{ is a bijection}\}$. Then $S \subseteq {}^{\mathbb{N}}\mathbb{N}$. So $S \preccurlyeq {}^{\mathbb{N}}\mathbb{N}$ by Note 1 following Example 7.3. By part (iv) of Problem 7, ${}^{\mathbb{N}}\mathbb{N} \sim \mathcal{P}(\mathbb{N})$. So, ${}^{\mathbb{N}}\mathbb{N} \preccurlyeq \mathcal{P}(\mathbb{N})$. By the transitivity of $\preccurlyeq$, $S \preccurlyeq \mathcal{P}(\mathbb{N})$.

Now, define $F\colon \mathcal{P}(\mathbb{N}) \to S$ by $F(A) = f_A$, where f_A is defined as follows: if $n \notin A$, then $f_A(2n) = 2n$ and $f_A(2n+1) = 2n+1$; if $n \in A$, then $f_A(2n) = 2n+1$ and $f_A(2n+1) = 2n$.

To see that F is injective, suppose that $A, B \in \mathcal{P}(\mathbb{N})$ and $A \neq B$. Without loss of generality, suppose that there is $n \in A \setminus B$. Then $f_A(2n) = 2n+1$ and $f_B(2n) = 2n$. So, $f_A \neq f_B$. Thus, $F(A) \neq F(B)$, and therefore, F is injective.

Since $S \preccurlyeq \mathcal{P}(\mathbb{N})$ and $\mathcal{P}(\mathbb{N}) \preccurlyeq S$, by the Cantor-Schroeder-Bernstein Theorem, $\mathcal{P}(\mathbb{N}) \sim S$. $\quad\square$

(ii) We first show that $\mathbb{R} \preccurlyeq {}^{\mathbb{N}}\mathbb{Q}$. Define $f\colon \mathbb{R} \to {}^{\mathbb{N}}\mathbb{Q}$ by $f(x) = (x_n)$, where (x_n) is some representative of x. Clearly, f is injective. It follows that

$$\mathbb{R} \preccurlyeq {}^{\mathbb{N}}\mathbb{Q} \subseteq \mathcal{P}(\mathbb{N} \times \mathbb{Q}) \sim \mathcal{P}(\mathbb{N} \times \mathbb{N}) \sim \mathcal{P}(\mathbb{N}).$$

Thus, $\mathbb{R} \preccurlyeq \mathcal{P}(\mathbb{N})$.

Next, we show that $\mathcal{P}(\mathbb{N}) \preccurlyeq \mathbb{R}$. Let $A \in \mathcal{P}(\mathbb{N})$. For each $n \in \mathbb{N}$, let $a_n = 0$ if $n \notin A$ and let $a_n = 1$ if $n \in A$. Let $a_n^* = \frac{a_0 a_1 \cdots a_n}{10^n}$. It is easy to check that (a_n^*) is a Cauchy sequence. Define $g\colon \mathcal{P}(\mathbb{N}) \to \mathbb{R}$ by $g(A) = [(a_n^*)]$. Then g is injective.

Since $\mathbb{R} \preccurlyeq \mathcal{P}(\mathbb{N})$ and $\mathcal{P}(\mathbb{N}) \preccurlyeq \mathbb{R}$, by the Cantor-Schroeder-Bernstein Theorem, we have $\mathbb{R} \sim \mathcal{P}(\mathbb{N})$. $\qquad\square$

(iii) By (ii), $\mathbb{R} \sim \mathcal{P}(\mathbb{N})$. By Problem 8, ${}^{\mathbb{N}}\mathbb{R} \sim {}^{\mathbb{N}}\mathcal{P}(\mathbb{N})$.

Using previous equinumerosity results, we get the following:

$$^{\mathbb{N}}\mathbb{R} \sim {}^{\mathbb{N}}\mathcal{P}(\mathbb{N}) \sim {}^{\mathbb{N}}({}^{\mathbb{N}}2) \sim {}^{\mathbb{N}\times\mathbb{N}}2 \sim {}^{\mathbb{N}}2 \sim \mathcal{P}(\mathbb{N}) \sim \mathbb{R} \prec \mathcal{P}(\mathbb{R}) \sim {}^{\mathbb{R}}2 \subseteq {}^{\mathbb{R}}\mathbb{N}. \text{ It follows that } {}^{\mathbb{N}}\mathbb{R} \prec {}^{\mathbb{R}}\mathbb{N}. \qquad \square$$

Note: To help us understand the function F defined in part (i) above, let's draw a visual representation of $F(\mathbb{E})$, where $\mathbb{E}$ is the set of even natural numbers.

Along the left of the image we have listed the natural numbers $0, 1, 2, 3, 4, \ldots$ (we stopped at 4, but our intention is that they keep going). The elements of $\mathbb{E}$ are $0, 2, 4, \ldots$ We highlighted these in bold. We associate each natural number n with the pair $\{2n, 2n + 1\}$. For example, $2 \cdot 4 = 8$ and $2 \cdot 4 + 1 = 9$. So, we associate 4 with the pair of natural numbers $\{8, 9\}$. We used left braces to indicate that association. The arrows give a visual representation of $f_{\mathbb{E}}$. Since $0 \in \mathbb{E}$, $f_{\mathbb{E}}$ swaps the corresponding pair 0 and 1. Since $1 \notin \mathbb{E}$, $f_{\mathbb{E}}$ leaves the corresponding pair 2 and 3 fixed. And so on, down the line…

The configuration of $f_{\mathbb{O}}$, where $\mathbb{O}$ is the set of odd natural numbers would be the opposite of the configuration for the evens. For example, 0 and 1 would remain fixed, while 2 and 3 would be swapped.

Problem Set 8

LEVEL 1

1. Use the Principle of Mathematical Induction to prove each of the following:

    (i) $2^n > n$ for all natural numbers $n \geq 1$.

    (ii) $0 + 1 + 2 + \cdots + n = \frac{n(n+1)}{2}$ for all natural numbers.

    (iii) $n! > 2^n$ for all natural numbers $n \geq 4$ (where $n! = 1 \cdot 2 \cdots n$ for all natural numbers $n \geq 1$).

    (iv) $2^n \geq n^2$ for all natural numbers $n \geq 4$.

Proofs:

(i)   **Base Case** $(k = 1)$: $2^1 = 2 > 1$.

Inductive Step: Let $k \in \mathbb{N}$ with $k \geq 1$ and assume that $2^k > k$. Then we have

$$2^{k+1} = 2^k \cdot 2^1 = 2^k \cdot 2 > k \cdot 2 = 2k = k + k \geq k + 1.$$

Therefore, $2^{k+1} > k + 1$.

By the Principle of Mathematical Induction, $2^n > n$ for all natural numbers $n \geq 1$. □

(ii) **Base Case** $(k = 0)$: $0 = \frac{0(0+1)}{2}$.

Inductive Step: Let $k \in \mathbb{N}$ and assume that $0 + 1 + 2 + \cdots + k = \frac{k(k+1)}{2}$. Then we have

$$0 + 1 + 2 + \cdots + k + (k+1) = \frac{k(k+1)}{2} + (k+1) = (k+1)\left(\frac{k}{2} + 1\right) = (k+1)\left(\frac{k}{2} + \frac{2}{2}\right)$$

$$= (k+1)\left(\frac{k+2}{2}\right) = \frac{(k+1)(k+2)}{2} = \frac{(k+1)\big((k+1)+1\big)}{2}$$

By the Principle of Mathematical Induction, $0 + 1 + 2 + \cdots + n = \frac{n(n+1)}{2}$ for all natural numbers n. □

(iii) **Base Case** $(k = 4)$: $4! = 1 \cdot 2 \cdot 3 \cdot 4 = 24 > 16 = 2^4$.

Inductive Step: Let $k \in \mathbb{N}$ with $k \geq 4$ and assume that $k! > 2^k$. Then we have

$$(k+1)! = (k+1)k! > (k+1)2^k \geq (4+1) \cdot 2^k = 5 \cdot 2^k \geq 2 \cdot 2^k = 2^1 \cdot 2^k = 2^{1+k} = 2^{k+1}.$$

Therefore, $(k+1)! > 2^{k+1}$.

By the Principle of Mathematical Induction, $n! > 2^n$ for all natural numbers $n \geq 4$. □

(iv) **Base Case** $(k = 4)$: $2^4 = 16 = 4^2$. So, $2^4 \geq 4^2$.

Inductive Step: Let $k \in \mathbb{N}$ with $k \geq 4$ and assume that $2^k \geq k^2$. Then we have

$$2^{k+1} = 2^k \cdot 2^1 \geq k^2 \cdot 2 = 2k^2 = k^2 + k^2.$$

By Theorem 8.8, $k^2 > 2k + 1$. So, we have $2^{k+1} > k^2 + 2k + 1 = (k + 1)^2$.

Therefore, $2^{k+1} \geq (k + 1)^2$.

By the Principle of Mathematical Induction, $2^n \geq n^2$ for all $n \in \mathbb{N}$ with $n \geq 4$. $\quad\square$

Note: Let's take one last look at number (iv). $2^0 = 1 \geq 0 = 0^2$. So, the statement in (iv) is true for $k = 0$. Also, $2^1 = 2 \geq 1 = 1^2$ and $2^2 = 4 = 2^2$. So, the statement is true for $k = 1$ and $k = 2$. However, $2^3 = 8$ and $3^2 = 9$. So, the statement is false for $k = 3$. It follows that $2^n \geq n^2$ for all natural numbers n except $n = 3$.

> 2. A natural number n is **divisible** by a natural number k, written $k|n$, if there is another natural number b such that $n = kb$. Prove that $n^3 - n$ is divisible by 3 for all natural numbers n.

Proof by Mathematical Induction:

Base Case $(k = 0)$: $0^3 - 0 = 0 = 3 \cdot 0$. So, $0^3 - 0$ is divisible by 3.

Inductive Step: Let $k \in \mathbb{N}$ and assume that $k^3 - k$ is divisible by 3. Then $k^3 - k = 3b$ for some integer b. Now,

$$(k + 1)^3 - (k + 1) = (k + 1)[(k + 1)^2 - 1] = (k + 1)[(k + 1)(k + 1) - 1]$$

$$= (k + 1)(k^2 + 2k + 1 - 1) = (k + 1)(k^2 + 2k) = k^3 + 2k^2 + k^2 + 2k = k^3 + 3k^2 + 2k$$

$$= k^3 - k + k + 3k^2 + 2k = (k^3 - k) + 3k^2 + 3k = 3b + 3(k^2 + k) = 3(b + k^2 + k).$$

Since $\mathbb{Z}$ is closed under addition and multiplication, $b + k^2 + k \in \mathbb{Z}$. Therefore, $(k + 1)^3 - (k + 1)$ is divisible by 3.

By the Principle of Mathematical Induction, $n^3 - n$ is divisible by 3 for all $n \in \mathbb{N}$. $\quad\square$

Note: Notice our use of SACT (see Note 7 following the proof of Theorem 8.5) in the beginning of the last line of the sequence of equations. We needed $k^3 - k$ to appear, but the $-k$ was nowhere to be found. So, we simply threw it in, and then repaired the damage by adding k right after it.

3. Prove each of the following. (You may assume that $<$ is a strict linear ordering of $\mathbb{N}$.)

    (i)   Addition is commutative in $\mathbb{N}$.

    (ii)   The set of natural numbers is closed under multiplication.

    (iii)   1 is a multiplicative identity in $\mathbb{N}$.

    (iv)   Multiplication is distributive over addition in $\mathbb{N}$.

    (v)   Multiplication is associative in $\mathbb{N}$.

    (vi)   Multiplication is commutative in $\mathbb{N}$.

    (vii)   For all natural numbers m, n, and k, if $m + k = n + k$, then $m = n$.

    (viii) For all natural numbers m, n, and k, if $mk = nk$, then $m = n$.

    (ix)   For all natural numbers m and n, $m < n$ if and only if there is a natural number $k > 0$ such that $n = m + k$.

    (x)   For all natural numbers m, n, and k, $m < n$ if and only if $m + k < n + k$.

    (xi)   For all natural numbers m and n, if $m > 0$ and $n > 0$, then $mn > 0$.

Proofs:

    (i)   We first prove by induction on n that $1 + n = n + 1$.

Base Case $(k = 0)$: By definition of addition of natural numbers, we have $1 + 0 = 1$. By Theorem 8.3, we have $0 + 1 = 1$. Therefore, $1 + 0 = 0 + 1$.

Inductive Step: Let $k \in \mathbb{N}$ and assume that $1 + k = k + 1$. Then we have

$$1 + (k + 1) = (1 + k) + 1 = (k + 1) + 1.$$

For the first equality, we used the definition of addition of natural numbers. For the second equality, we used the inductive hypothesis.

By the Principle of Mathematical Induction, for all natural numbers n, $1 + n = n + 1$.

We are now ready to use induction to prove the result. Assume that m is a natural number.

Base Case $(k = 0)$: By definition of addition of natural numbers, $m + 0 = m$. By Theorem 8.3, $0 + m = m$. Therefore, $m + 0 = 0 + m$.

Inductive Step: Let $k \in \mathbb{N}$ and assume that $m + k = k + m$. Then we have

$$m + (k + 1) = (m + k) + 1 = (k + m) + 1 = k + (m + 1) = k + (1 + m) = (k + 1) + m.$$

For the first and third equalities, we used the definition of addition of natural numbers (or Theorem 8.4). For the second equality, we used the inductive hypothesis. For the fourth equality, we used the preliminary result that we proved above. For the fifth equality, we used Theorem 8.4.

By the Principle of Mathematical Induction, for all natural numbers n, $m + n = n + m$.

Since m was an arbitrary natural number, we have shown that for all natural numbers m and n, we have $m + n = n + m$. □

   (ii)   Assume that m is a natural number.

Base Case $(k = 0)$: $m \cdot 0 = 0$, which is a natural number.

Inductive Step: Let k be a natural number and assume that mk is also a natural number. Then $m(k + 1) = mk + m$. Since mk and m are both natural numbers, by Theorem 8.2, $mk + m$ is a natural number.

By the Principle of Mathematical Induction, mn is a natural number for all natural numbers n.

Since m was an arbitrary natural number, we have shown that the product of any two natural numbers is a natural number. □

   (iii)   Assume that m is a natural number.

We have $m \cdot 1 = m(0 + 1) = m \cdot 0 + m = 0 + m = m$. For the first and fourth equalities, we used Theorem 8.3. For the second and third equalities, we used the definition of multiplication of natural numbers.

We prove that $1 \cdot n = n$ by induction on n.

Proof: Base Case $(k = 0)$: $1 \cdot 0 = 0$ by the definition of multiplication of natural numbers.

Inductive Step: Let $k \in \mathbb{N}$ and assume that $1 \cdot k = k$. Then

$$1(k + 1) = 1 \cdot k + 1 = k + 1.$$

For the first equality, we used the definition of multiplication of natural numbers. For the second equality, we used the inductive hypothesis.

By the Principle of Mathematical Induction, for all natural numbers n, $1 \cdot n = n$. □

   (iv)   Let m and n be natural numbers. We first prove that for all $t \in \mathbb{N}$, $(m + n) \cdot t = mt + nt$ (we say that multiplication is **right distributive** over addition in $\mathbb{N}$).

Base Case $(k = 0)$: $(m + n) \cdot 0 = 0$ by the definition of multiplication of natural numbers. Similarly, $m \cdot 0 = 0$ and $n \cdot 0 = 0$. So, $m \cdot 0 + n \cdot 0 = 0$. Therefore, $(m + n) \cdot 0 = m \cdot 0 + n \cdot 0$.

Inductive Step: Let $k \in \mathbb{N}$ and assume that $(m + n) \cdot k = mk + nk$. Then

$$(m + n)(k + 1) = (m + n) \cdot k + (m + n) = (mk + nk) + (m + n)$$
$$= (mk + m) + (nk + n) = m(k + 1) + n(k + 1).$$

For the first and fourth equalities, we used the definition of multiplication of natural numbers. For the second equality, we used the inductive hypothesis. For the third equality we used the fact that addition is associative and commutative in $\mathbb{N}$ several times.

By the Principle of Mathematical Induction, for all natural numbers t, $(m + n) \cdot t = mt + nt$.

We next prove that $n \cdot 0 = 0$ and $0 \cdot n = 0$ for all natural numbers n.

$n \cdot 0 = 0$ by the definition of multiplication of natural numbers.

We prove that $0 \cdot n = 0$ by induction on n.

Base Case $(k = 0)$: By definition of multiplication of natural numbers, we have $0 \cdot 0 = 0$.

Inductive Step: Let $k \in \mathbb{N}$ and assume that $0 \cdot k = 0$. Then we have

$$0 \cdot (k + 1) = 0 \cdot k + 0 = 0 + 0 = 0.$$

For the first equality, we used the definition of multiplication of natural numbers. For the second equality, we used the inductive hypothesis. For the third equality, we used the definition of addition of natural numbers.

By the Principle of Mathematical Induction, for all natural numbers n, $0 \cdot n = n$.

Let m be a natural number. We prove that for all $n \in \mathbb{N}$, $mn = nm$ (we say that multiplication is **commutative** in $\mathbb{N}$).

Base Case $(k = 0)$: $m \cdot 0 = 0$ by the definition of multiplication of natural numbers. We just proved that $0 \cdot m = 0$. Therefore, $m \cdot 0 = 0 \cdot m$

Inductive Step: Let $k \in \mathbb{N}$ and assume that $mk = km$. Then

$$m(k + 1) = mk + m = km + m = (k + 1)m.$$

For the first equality, we used the definition of multiplication of natural numbers. For the second equality, we used the inductive hypothesis. For the third equality we used the fact that multiplication is right distributive over addition in $\mathbb{N}$ (proved above).

By the Principle of Mathematical Induction, for all natural numbers n, $mn = nm$.

Finally, let $m, n, t \in \mathbb{N}$. Then $m(n + t) = (n + t)m = nm + tm = mn + mt$. This shows that multiplication is distributive over addition in $\mathbb{N}$. $\qquad\square$

(v)   Assume that m and n are natural numbers

Base Case $(k = 0)$: $(mn) \cdot 0 = 0 = m \cdot 0 = m(n \cdot 0)$ by the definition of multiplication of natural numbers.

Inductive Step: Let $k \in \mathbb{N}$ and assume that $(mn)k = m(nk)$. Then

$$(mn)(k + 1) = (mn)k + mn = m(nk) + mn = mn + m(nk)$$
$$= m(n + nk) = m(nk + n) = m\big(n(k + 1)\big).$$

For the first and sixth equalities, we used the definition of multiplication of natural numbers. For the second equality, we used the inductive hypothesis. For the third and fifth equalities, we used the fact that addition is commutative in $\mathbb{N}$. For the fourth equality, we used the fact that multiplication is distributive over addition in $\mathbb{N}$.

By the Principle of Mathematical Induction, for all natural numbers t, $(mn)t = m(nt)$. This shows that multiplication is associative in $\mathbb{N}$. $\qquad\square$

(vi)   This was already proved in (iv) above. $\qquad\square$

(vii)   Let $m, n \in \mathbb{N}$. We prove by induction on k that $m + k = n + k \rightarrow m = n$.

Base Case ($k = 0$ and $k = 1$): If $m + 0 = n + 0$, then since $m + 0 = m$ and $n + 0 = n$ (by definition of addition of natural numbers), $m = n$. Next, suppose $m + 1 = n + 1$. Then $m \cup \{m\} = n \cup \{n\}$. If $n \neq m$, then either $n \in m$ or $m \in n$. Without loss of generality, assume that $n \in m$. Since $\in$ is antisymmetric on $\mathbb{N}$ and $n \neq m$, we must have $m \notin n$. Thus, $m = n$, contrary to our assumption that $n \neq m$. This contradiction shows that $m = n$.

Inductive Step: Let $t \in \mathbb{N}$, assume that $m + t = n + t \rightarrow m = n$, and let $m + (t + 1) = n + (t + 1)$. By the definition of addition in $\mathbb{N}$, $(m + t) + 1 = (n + t) + 1$. By the base case, $m + t = n + t$. By the inductive hypothesis, $m = n$.

By the Principle of Mathematical Induction, for all natural numbers m, n, and k, if $m + k = n + k$, then $m = n$. $\qquad\square$

(viii)   Let $m, n \in \mathbb{N}$. We prove by induction on k that $mk = nk \rightarrow m = n$.

Base Case ($k = 0$): If $m \cdot 0 = n \cdot 0$, then since $m \cdot 0 = 0$ and $n \cdot 0 = 0$ (by definition of multiplication of natural numbers), $m = n$.

Inductive Step: Let $t \in \mathbb{N}$, assume that $mt = nt \rightarrow m = n$, and let $m(t + 1) = n(t + 1)$. By the definition of multiplication in $\mathbb{N}$, $mt + 1 = nt + 1$. By (vii), $mt = nt$. By the inductive hypothesis, we have $m = n$.

By the Principle of Mathematical Induction, for all natural numbers m, n, and k, if $mk = nk$, then $m = n$. $\qquad\square$

(ix)   Let $m \in \mathbb{N}$. We prove by induction on n that if $m < n$, there is $k > 0$ such that $n = m + k$.

Base Case ($t = 0$): If $m < 0$, then $m \in \emptyset$, which is impossible. So, the conclusion is vacuously true.

Inductive Step: Let $t \in \mathbb{N}$ and assume that if $m < t$, there is $k > 0$ such that $t = m + k$. Assume that $m < t + 1$. Then $m < t$ or $m = t$. If $m < t$, then $t + 1 = (m + k) + 1 = m + (k + 1)$. If $m = t$, then $t + 1 = m + 1$.

By the Principle of Mathematical Induction, for all $n \in \mathbb{N}$, if $m < n$, there is $k > 0$ so that $n = m + k$.

Now, let $n, m \in \mathbb{N}$. We prove by induction on $k > 0$ that if $n = m + k$, then $m < n$.

Base Case ($t = 1$): If $n = m + 1 = m \cup \{m\}$, then since $m \in \{m\}$, $m \in n$, and so, $m < n$.

Inductive Step: Assume that if $n = m + t$, then $m < n$. Let $n = m + (t + 1)$. Then since addition is commutative and associative in $\mathbb{N}$, $n = m + (1 + t) = (m + 1) + t$. By the inductive hypothesis, we have $m + 1 < n$. Since $m < m + 1$ and $<$ is transitive on $\mathbb{N}$, $m < n$.

By the Principle of Mathematical Induction, if $k > 0$ and $n = m + k$, then $m < n$. $\qquad\square$

(x)   Let $m, n, k \in \mathbb{N}$.

By (ix), $m < n$ if and only if there is a natural number $t > 0$ such that $n = m + t$. Now, $n + k = (m + t) + k = m + (t + k) = m + (k + t) = (m + k) + t$. So, if $m < n$, then there is a natural number $t > 0$ such that $n + k = (m + k) + t$. Thus, by (ix), $m + k < n + k$. Conversely, if $m + k < n + k$, then there is a natural number t such that $n + k = (m + k) + t = (m + t) + k$. By (vii), $n = m + t$. So, by (ix) again, $m < n$. $\qquad\square$

46

(xi) Let $m \in \mathbb{N}$ with $m > 0$. We prove by induction on n that $n > 0 \rightarrow mn > 0$.

Base Case ($k = 1$): If $n = 1$, then $m \cdot 1 = m \cdot 0 + m = 0 + m = m > 0$.

Inductive Step: Let $k \in \mathbb{N}$ with $k > 0$ and assume that $mk > 0$. Then $m(k + 1) = mk + k$. Since $mk > 0$, by (x), $mk + k > 0 + k = k > 0$. So, $m(k + 1) > 0$.

By the Principle of Mathematical Induction, for all natural numbers m and n, if $m > 0$ and $n > 0$, then $mn > 0$. □

4. A set A is **transitive** if $\forall x (x \in A \rightarrow x \subseteq A)$ (in words, every element of A is also a subset of A). Prove that every natural number is transitive.

Proof by Mathematical Induction:

Base Case ($k = 0$): $0 = \emptyset$. Since $\emptyset$ has no elements, it is vacuously true that every element of $\emptyset$ is a subset of $\emptyset$.

Inductive Step: Assuming that k is transitive, let $j \in k + 1 = k \cup \{k\}$ and $m \in j$. Then $j \in k$ or $j \in \{k\}$. If $j \in k$, then we have $m \in j \in k$. Since k is transitive, $m \in k$. Therefore, $m \in k \cup \{k\} = k + 1$. If $j \in \{k\}$, then $j = k$. So, $m \in k$, and again, $m \in k \cup \{k\} = k + 1$.

By the Principle of Mathematical Induction, every natural number is transitive. □

LEVEL 3

5. Prove that if $n \in \mathbb{N}$ and A is a nonempty subset of n, then A has a least element.

Proof by Mathematical Induction:

Base Case ($k = 0$): $0 = \emptyset$. The only subset of $\emptyset$ is $\emptyset$. So, the statement is vacuously true.

Inductive Step: Assume that every nonempty subset of the natural number k has a least element. We will show that every nonempty subset of $k + 1 = k \cup \{k\}$ has a least element.

Let A be a nonempty subset of $k + 1$. Then $A \setminus \{k\} \subseteq k$. If $A \setminus \{k\} \neq \emptyset$, then by the inductive hypothesis, $A \setminus \{k\}$ has a least element, say j. Since $j \in k$, j is the least element of A. If $A \setminus \{k\} = \emptyset$, then k is the only element of A, and therefore, it is the least element of A.

By the Principle of Mathematical Induction, if $n \in \mathbb{N}$ and A is a nonempty subset of n, then A has a least element. □

6. Prove POMI → WOP.

Proof: Assume POMI, let A be a nonempty subset of $\mathbb{N}$, and choose $n \in A$. If $n \cap A = \emptyset$, then n is the least element of A (If $m \in A$ with $m \in n$, then $m \in n \cap A$, contradicting $n \cap A = \emptyset$). Otherwise, $n \cap A$ is a nonempty subset of n, and so, by Problem 5, $n \cap A$ has a least element m. Then m is the least element of A (If $k \in A$ with $k \in m$, then $k \in n$ by Problem 4, and so, m is not the least element of $n \cap A$). □

LEVEL 4

7. Prove that $3^n - 1$ is even for all natural numbers n.

Proof by Mathematical Induction:

Base Case $(k = 0)$: $3^0 - 1 = 1 - 1 = 0 = 2 \cdot 0$. So, $3^0 - 1$ is even.

Inductive Step: Let $k \in \mathbb{N}$ and assume that $3^k - 1$ is even. Then $3^k - 1 = 2b$ for some integer b. Now,

$$3^{k+1} - 1 = 3^k \cdot 3^1 - 1 = 3^k \cdot 3 - 1 = 3^k \cdot 3 - 3^k + 3^k - 1 = 3^k(3 - 1) + (3^k - 1)$$

$$= 3^k \cdot 2 + 2b = 2 \cdot 3^k + 2b = 2(3^k + b).$$

Since $\mathbb{N}$ is closed under multiplication, $3^k \in \mathbb{N}$. Since $\mathbb{N}$ is closed under addition, $3^k + b \in \mathbb{N}$. Therefore, $3^{k+1} - 1$ is even.

By the Principle of Mathematical Induction, $3^n - 1$ is even for all $n \in \mathbb{N}$. $\qquad\square$

Notes: Notice our use of SACT (see Note 7 following the proof of Theorem 8.5) in the middle of the first line of the sequence of equations. We needed $3^k - 1$ to appear, so we added 3^k, and then subtracted 3^k to the left of it.

8. Show that the Principle of Mathematical Induction is equivalent to the following statement:

   $(\star)$ Let $P(n)$ be a statement and suppose that (i) $P(0)$ is true and (ii) for all $k \in \mathbb{N}$, $P(k) \to P(k+1)$. Then $P(n)$ is true for all $n \in \mathbb{N}$.

Proof: Recall that the Principle of Mathematical Induction says the following: Let S be a set of natural numbers such that (i) $0 \in S$ and (ii) for all $k \in \mathbb{N}$, $k \in S \to k + 1 \in S$. Then $S = \mathbb{N}$.

Suppose that the Principle of Mathematical Induction is true and let $P(n)$ be a statement such that $P(0)$ is true, and for all $k \in \mathbb{N}$, $P(k) \to P(k+1)$. Define $S = \{n \mid (P(n)\}$. Since $P(0)$ is true, $0 \in S$. If $k \in S$, then $P(k)$ is true. So, $P(k+1)$ is true, and therefore, $k + 1 \in S$. By the Principle of Mathematical Induction, $S = \mathbb{N}$. So, $P(n)$ is true for all $n \in \mathbb{N}$.

Now, suppose that $(\star)$ holds, and let S be a set of natural numbers such that $0 \in S$, and for all $k \in \mathbb{N}$, $k \in S \to k + 1 \in S$. Let $P(n)$ be the statement $n \in S$. Since $0 \in S$, $P(0)$ is true. If $P(k)$ is true, then $k \in S$. So, $k + 1 \in S$, and therefore, $P(k+1)$ is true. By $(\star)$, $P(n)$ is true for all n. So, for all $n \in \mathbb{N}$, we have $n \in S$. In other words, $\mathbb{N} \subseteq S$. Since we were given $S \subseteq \mathbb{N}$, we have $S = \mathbb{N}$. $\qquad\square$

LEVEL 5

9. The Principle of Strong Induction is the following statement:

   $(\star\star)$ Let $P(n)$ be a statement and suppose that (i) $P(0)$ is true and (ii) for all $k \in \mathbb{N}$, $\forall j \leq k \, (P(j)) \to P(k+1)$. Then $P(n)$ is true for all $n \in \mathbb{N}$.

   Use the Principle of Mathematical Induction to prove the Principle of Strong Induction.

Proof: Let $P(n)$ be a statement such that $P(0)$ is true, and for all $k \in \mathbb{N}$, $\forall j \leq k \left(P(j)\right) \rightarrow P(k+1)$. Let $Q(n)$ be the statement $\forall j \leq n \left(P(j)\right)$.

Base case: $Q(0) \equiv \forall j \leq 0 \left(P(j)\right) \equiv P(0)$. Since $P(0)$ is true and $Q(0) \equiv P(0)$, $Q(0)$ is also true.

Inductive step: Suppose that $Q(k)$ is true. Then $\forall j \leq k \left(P(j)\right)$ is true. Therefore, $P(k+1)$ is true. So $Q(k) \wedge P(k+1)$ is true. But notice that

$$Q(k+1) \equiv \forall j \leq k+1 \left(P(j)\right) \equiv \forall j \leq k \left(P(j)\right) \wedge P(k+1) \equiv Q(k) \wedge P(k+1).$$

So, $Q(k+1)$ is true.

By the Principle of Mathematical Induction $((\star)$ from Problem 8), $Q(n)$ is true for all $n \in \mathbb{N}$. This implies that $P(n)$ is true for all $n \in \mathbb{N}$. $\qquad\square$

> 10. Use the Principle of Mathematical Induction to prove that for every $n \in \mathbb{N}$, if S is a set with $|S| = n$, then S has 2^n subsets. (Hint: Use Problem 10 from Problem Set 2.)

Proof: Base Case $(k = 0)$: Let S be a set with $|S| = 0$. Then $S = \emptyset$, and the empty set has exactly 1 subset, namely itself. So, the number of subsets of S is $1 = 2^0$.

Inductive Step: Assume that for any set S with $|S| = k$, S has 2^k subsets.

Now, let A be a set with $|A| = k + 1$, let d be any element from A, and let $S = A \setminus \{d\}$ (S is the set consisting of all elements of A except d). $|S| = k$, and so, by the inductive hypothesis, S has 2^k subsets. Let $B = \{X \mid X \subseteq A \wedge d \notin X\}$ and $C = \{X \mid X \subseteq A \wedge d \in X\}$. B is precisely the set of subsets of S, and so $|B| = 2^k$. By Problem 10 from Lesson 2, $|B| = |C|$ and therefore, $|C| = 2^k$. Also, B and C have no elements in common and every subset of A is in either B or C. So, the number of subsets of A is equal to $|B| + |C| = 2^k + 2^k = 2 \cdot 2^k = 2^1 \cdot 2^k = 2^{1+k} = 2^{k+1}$.

By the Principle of Mathematical Induction, given any $n \in \mathbb{N}$, if S is a set with $|S| = n$, then S has 2^n subsets. $\qquad\square$

Notes: (1) Recall from Lesson 1 that $|S| = n$ means that the set S has n elements.

(2) Recall from Lesson 2 that if S is a set, then the **power set** of S is the set of subsets of S.

$$\mathcal{P}(S) = \{X \mid X \subseteq S\}$$

In this problem, we proved that a set with n elements has a power set with 2^n elements. Symbolically, we have

$$|S| = n \rightarrow |\mathcal{P}(S)| = 2^n.$$

Problem Set 9

LEVEL 1

1. Let p, q, and r represent true statements. Compute the truth value of each of the following compound statements:

    (i) $(p \lor q) \lor r$

    (ii) $(p \lor q) \land \neg r$

    (iii) $\neg p \to (q \lor r)$

    (iv) $\neg(p \leftrightarrow \neg q) \land r$

    (v) $\neg[p \land (\neg q \to r)]$

    (vi) $\neg[(\neg p \lor \neg q) \leftrightarrow \neg r]$

    (vii) $p \to (q \to \neg r)$

    (viii) $\neg[\neg p \to (q \to \neg r)]$

Solutions:

(i) $(p \lor q) \lor r \equiv (T \lor T) \lor T \equiv T \lor T \equiv \mathbf{T}$.

(ii) $(p \lor q) \land \neg r \equiv (T \lor T) \land \neg T \equiv T \land F \equiv \mathbf{F}$.

(iii) $\neg p \to (q \lor r) \equiv \neg T \to (T \lor T) \equiv F \to T \equiv \mathbf{T}$.

(iv) $\neg(p \leftrightarrow \neg q) \land r \equiv \neg(T \leftrightarrow \neg T) \land T \equiv \neg(T \leftrightarrow F) \land T \equiv \neg F \land T \equiv T \land T \equiv \mathbf{T}$.

(v) $\neg[p \land (\neg q \to r)] \equiv \neg[T \land (\neg T \to T)] \equiv \neg[T \land (F \to T)] \equiv \neg[T \land T] \equiv \neg T \equiv \mathbf{F}$.

(vi) $\neg[(\neg p \lor \neg q) \leftrightarrow \neg r] \equiv \neg[(\neg T \lor \neg T) \leftrightarrow \neg T] \equiv \neg[(F \lor F) \leftrightarrow F] \equiv \neg[F \leftrightarrow F] \equiv \neg T \equiv \mathbf{F}$.

(vii) $p \to (q \to \neg r) \equiv T \to (T \to \neg T) \equiv T \to (T \to F) \equiv T \to F \equiv \mathbf{F}$.

(viii) $\neg[\neg p \to (q \to \neg r)] \equiv \neg[\neg T \to (T \to \neg T)] \equiv \neg[F \to (T \to F)] \equiv \neg[F \to F] \equiv \neg T \equiv \mathbf{F}$.

Notes: (1) We began each of these problems by replacing the propositional variables p, q, and r by their given truth values (all T). We could save a little time in each case by replacing the negations of each of the propositional variables by F right away. For example. (ii) above would look as follows:

(ii) $(p \lor q) \land \neg r \equiv (T \lor T) \land F \equiv T \land F \equiv \mathbf{F}$.

(2) At each step, we used the truth table of the appropriate connective. For example, in problem (v) to get $\neg[T \land (F \to T)] \equiv \neg[T \land T]$, we used the third row of the truth table for the conditional.

p	q	$p \to q$
T	T	T
T	F	F
F	T	T
F	F	T

We see from the highlighted row that $F \to T \equiv T$, and therefore $\neg[T \wedge (F \to T)] \equiv \neg[T \wedge T]$.

Quicker solutions:

(i)　$(p \vee q) \vee r \equiv (p \vee q) \vee T \equiv \mathbf{T}$.

(ii)　$(p \vee q) \wedge \neg r \equiv (p \vee q) \wedge F \equiv \mathbf{F}$.

(iii)　$\neg p \to (q \vee r) \equiv F \to (q \vee r) \equiv \mathbf{T}$.

(iv)　$\neg(p \leftrightarrow \neg q) \wedge r \equiv \neg(T \leftrightarrow F) \wedge T \equiv \neg F \wedge T \equiv T \wedge T \equiv \mathbf{T}$.

(v)　$\neg[p \wedge (\neg q \to r)] \equiv \neg[p \wedge (F \to r)] \equiv \neg[p \wedge T] \equiv \neg[T \wedge T] \equiv \neg T \equiv \mathbf{F}$.

(vi)　$\neg[(\neg p \vee \neg q) \leftrightarrow \neg r] \equiv \neg[F \leftrightarrow F] \equiv \neg T \equiv \mathbf{F}$.

(vii)　$p \to (q \to \neg r) \equiv T \to (T \to F) \equiv T \to F \equiv \mathbf{F}$.

(viii)　$\neg[\neg p \to (q \to \neg r)] \equiv \neg[F \to (q \to \neg r)] \equiv \neg T \equiv \mathbf{F}$.

2. Let ϕ be the following statement: $(p \wedge \neg q) \leftrightarrow \neg[p \vee (\neg r \to q)]$.

   (i)　The statement ϕ is abbreviated. Write ϕ in its unabbreviated form.

   (ii)　Write down all the substatements of ϕ in both abbreviated and unabbreviated form.

Solutions:

(i)　$\left((p \wedge (\neg q)) \leftrightarrow \left(\neg[p \vee ((\neg r) \to q)] \right) \right)$

(ii)　Abbreviated forms: $p, q, r, \neg q, \neg r, p \wedge \neg q, \neg r \to q, p \vee (\neg r \to q), \neg[p \vee (\neg r \to q)]$

Unabbreviated forms: $p, q, r, (\neg q), (\neg r), (p \wedge (\neg q)), ((\neg r) \to q), \left(p \vee ((\neg r) \to q) \right),$
$\left(\neg[p \vee ((\neg r) \to q)] \right)$

LEVEL 2

3. Consider the compound statement "You can have a cookie or ice cream." In English this would most likely mean that you can have one or the other but not both. The word "or" used here is generally called an "exclusive or" because it excludes the possibility of both. The disjunction is an "inclusive or." Using the symbol $\oplus$ for exclusive or, draw the truth table for this connective. Then using only the logical connectives $\neg$, $\wedge$, and $\vee$, produce a statement using the propositional variables p and q that has the same truth table as $p \oplus q$.

Solution:

p	q	$p \oplus q$
T	T	F
T	F	T
F	T	T
F	F	F

Now, we want to express that p is true or q is true, but p and q are not both true. Expressed in symbols, this is $(p \vee q) \wedge \neg(p \wedge q)$.

Note: (1) Let's check that $(p \vee q) \wedge \neg(p \wedge q)$ behaves as desired.

If p and q are both true, then $\neg(p \wedge q) \equiv F$, and so $(p \vee q) \wedge \neg(p \wedge q) \equiv (p \vee q) \wedge F \equiv F$.

If p and q are both false, then $p \vee q \equiv F$, and so $(p \vee q) \wedge \neg(p \wedge q) \equiv F \wedge \neg(p \wedge q) \equiv F$.

Finally, if p and q have opposite truth values, then $p \vee q \equiv T$ and $\neg(p \wedge q) \equiv T$ (because $p \wedge q \equiv F$). Therefore, $(p \vee q) \wedge \neg(p \wedge q) \equiv T \wedge T \equiv T$.

(2) In propositional logic, the word "but" has the same meaning as the word "and." In English, the word "but" is used to introduce contrast with the part of the sentence that has already been mentioned. However, logically it is no different than "and."

(3) Another way to see that $p \oplus q$ has the same truth values as $(p \vee q) \wedge \neg(p \wedge q)$ is to draw the truth tables for each and observe that row by row they have the same truth values. We do this below.

p	q	$p \oplus q$	$p \vee q$	$p \wedge q$	$\neg(p \wedge q)$	$(p \vee q) \wedge \neg(p \wedge q)$
T	T	F	T	T	F	F
T	F	T	T	F	T	T
F	T	T	T	F	T	T
F	F	F	F	F	T	F

Observe that the third column of the truth table corresponds to $p \oplus q$, the last (seventh) column corresponds to $(p \vee q) \wedge \neg(p \wedge q)$, and both these columns have the same truth values.

(4) In this problem, we showed that $p \oplus q \equiv (p \vee q) \wedge \neg(p \wedge q)$.

4. Verify all the logical equivalences in List 9.1 and all the rules of inference in List 9.2.

Solutions:

1. **Law of double negation:** $p \equiv \neg(\neg p)$: This was done in Example 9.5.

2. **De Morgan's laws:** $\neg(p \wedge q) \equiv \neg p \vee \neg q$: This was done in Example 9.6

   $\neg(p \vee q) \equiv \neg p \wedge \neg q$: Let $\phi = \neg(p \vee q)$ and let $\psi = \neg p \wedge \neg q$. If $p \equiv T$ or $q \equiv T$, then $\phi \equiv \neg T \equiv F$ and $\psi \equiv F$ (because $\neg p \equiv F$ or $\neg q \equiv F$). If $p \equiv F$ and $q \equiv F$, then $\phi \equiv \neg F \equiv T$ and $\psi \equiv T \wedge T \equiv T$. So, all four possible truth assignments of p and q lead to the same truth value for ϕ and ψ. It follows that $\phi \equiv \psi$.

3. **Commutative laws:** $p \wedge q \equiv q \wedge p, p \vee q \equiv q \vee p$: Look at the truth tables.

4. **Associative laws:** $(p \wedge q) \wedge r \equiv p \wedge (q \wedge r), (p \vee q) \vee r \equiv p \vee (q \vee r)$: Draw truth tables.

5. **Distributive laws:** $p \wedge (q \vee r) \equiv (p \wedge q) \vee (p \wedge r), p \vee (q \wedge r) \equiv (p \vee q) \wedge (p \vee r)$: Draw truth tables.

6. **Identity laws:** $p \wedge T \equiv p$: Let $\phi = p \wedge T$ and let $\psi = p$. If $p \equiv T$, then $\phi \equiv T \wedge T \equiv T$ and $\psi \equiv T$. If $p \equiv F$, then $\phi \equiv F \wedge T \equiv F$ and $\psi \equiv F$. So, both possible truth assignments of p lead to the same truth value for ϕ and ψ. It follows that $\phi \equiv \psi$.

   $p \wedge F \equiv F$: Let $\phi = p \wedge F$ and let $\psi = F$. If $p \equiv T$, then $\phi \equiv T \wedge F \equiv F$ and $\psi \equiv F$. If $p \equiv F$, then $\phi \equiv F \wedge F \equiv F$ and $\psi \equiv F$. So, both possible truth assignments of p lead to the same truth value for ϕ and ψ. It follows that $\phi \equiv \psi$.

   $p \vee T \equiv T$: Let $\phi = p \vee T$ and let $\psi = T$. If $p \equiv T$, then $\phi \equiv T \vee T \equiv T$ and $\psi \equiv T$. If $p \equiv F$, then $\phi \equiv F \vee T \equiv T$ and $\psi \equiv T$. So, both possible truth assignments of p lead to the same truth value for ϕ and ψ. It follows that $\phi \equiv \psi$.

   $p \vee F \equiv p$: Let $\phi = p \vee F$ and let $\psi = p$. If $p \equiv T$, then $\phi \equiv T \vee F \equiv T$ and $\psi \equiv T$. If $p \equiv F$, then $\phi \equiv F \vee F \equiv F$ and $\psi \equiv F$. So, both possible truth assignments of p lead to the same truth value for ϕ and ψ. It follows that $\phi \equiv \psi$.

7. **Negation laws:** $p \wedge \neg p \equiv F$: Let $\phi = p \wedge \neg p$ and let $\psi = F$. If $p \equiv T$, then $\phi \equiv T \wedge F \equiv F$ and $\psi \equiv F$. If $p \equiv F$, then $\phi \equiv F \wedge T \equiv F$ and $\psi \equiv F$. So, both possible truth assignments of p lead to the same truth value for ϕ and ψ. It follows that $\phi \equiv \psi$.

   $p \vee \neg p \equiv T$: Let $\phi = p \vee \neg p$ and let $\psi = T$. If $p \equiv T$, then $\phi \equiv T \vee F \equiv T$ and $\psi \equiv T$. If $p \equiv F$, then $\phi \equiv F \vee T \equiv T$ and $\psi \equiv T$. So, both possible truth assignments of p lead to the same truth value for ϕ and ψ. It follows that $\phi \equiv \psi$.

8. **Redundancy laws:** $p \wedge p \equiv p$: Let $\phi = p \wedge p$ and let $\psi = p$. If $p \equiv T$, then $\phi \equiv T \wedge T \equiv T$ and $\psi \equiv T$. If $p \equiv F$, then $\phi \equiv F \wedge F \equiv F$ and $\psi \equiv F$. So, both possible truth assignments of p lead to the same truth value for ϕ and ψ. It follows that $\phi \equiv \psi$.

   $p \vee p \equiv p$: Let $\phi = p \vee p$ and let $\psi = p$. If $p \equiv T$, then $\phi \equiv T \vee T \equiv T$ and $\psi \equiv T$. If $p \equiv F$, then $\phi \equiv F \vee F \equiv F$ and $\psi \equiv F$. So, both possible truth assignments of p lead to the same truth value for ϕ and ψ. It follows that $\phi \equiv \psi$.

   Absorption laws: $(p \vee q) \wedge p \equiv p$: Let $\phi = (p \vee q) \wedge p$ and let $\psi = p$. If $p \equiv T$, then $p \vee q \equiv T \vee q \equiv T$. So, $\phi \equiv T \wedge T \equiv T$. Also, $\psi \equiv T$. If $p \equiv F$, then $\phi \equiv (p \vee q) \wedge F \equiv F$ and $\psi \equiv F$. So, all four possible truth assignments of p and q lead to the same truth value for ϕ and ψ. It follows that $\phi \equiv \psi$.

   $(p \wedge q) \vee p \equiv p$: Let $\phi = (p \wedge q) \vee p$ and let $\psi = p$. If $p \equiv T$, then $\phi \equiv (p \wedge q) \vee T \equiv T$ and $\psi \equiv T$. If $p \equiv F$, then $p \wedge q \equiv F \wedge q \equiv F$. So, $\phi \equiv F \vee F \equiv F$. Also, $\psi \equiv F$. So, all four possible truth assignments of p and q lead to the same truth value for ϕ and ψ. It follows that $\phi \equiv \psi$.

9. **Law of the conditional:** $p \rightarrow q \equiv \neg p \vee q$: Let $\phi = p \rightarrow q$ and let $\psi = \neg p \vee q$. If $p \equiv F$, then $\phi \equiv F \rightarrow q \equiv T$ and $\psi \equiv T \vee q \equiv T$. If $q \equiv T$, then $\phi \equiv p \rightarrow T \equiv T$ and $\psi \equiv \neg p \vee T \equiv T$. Finally, if $p \equiv T$ and $q \equiv F$, then $\phi \equiv T \rightarrow F \equiv F$ and $\psi \equiv F \vee F \equiv F$. So, all four possible truth assignments of p and q lead to the same truth value for ϕ and ψ. It follows that $\phi \equiv \psi$.

10. **Law of the contrapositive:** $p \rightarrow q \equiv \neg q \rightarrow \neg p$: Let $\phi = p \rightarrow q$ and let $\psi = \neg q \rightarrow \neg p$. If $p \equiv F$, then $\phi \equiv F \rightarrow q \equiv T$ and $\psi \equiv \neg q \rightarrow T \equiv T$. If $q \equiv T$, then $\phi \equiv p \rightarrow T \equiv T$ and $\psi \equiv F \rightarrow \neg p \equiv T$. Finally, if $p \equiv T$ and $q \equiv F$, then $\phi \equiv T \rightarrow F \equiv F$ and $\psi \equiv T \rightarrow F \equiv F$. So, all four possible truth assignments of p and q lead to the same truth value for ϕ and ψ. It follows that $\phi \equiv \psi$.

11. **Law of the biconditional:** $p \leftrightarrow q \equiv (p \to q) \wedge (q \to p)$: Let $\phi = p \leftrightarrow q$ and let $\psi = (p \to q) \wedge (q \to p)$. If $p \equiv T$, then $\phi \equiv T \leftrightarrow q \equiv q$, $\psi \equiv (T \to q) \wedge (q \to T) \equiv q \wedge T \equiv q$. If $p \equiv F$, $\phi \equiv F \leftrightarrow q \equiv \neg q$, $\psi \equiv (F \to q) \wedge (q \to F) \equiv T \wedge \neg q \equiv \neg q$. So, all four possible truth assignments of p and q lead to the same truth value for ϕ and ψ. It follows that $\phi \equiv \psi$.

Modus Ponens	Modus Tollens	Disjunctive Syllogism	Hypothetical Syllogism
$p \to q$	$p \to q$	$p \vee q$	$p \to q$
p	$\neg q$	$\neg p$	$q \to r$
q	$\neg p$	q	$p \to r$

Modus Ponens: This was done in Example 9.8.

Modus Tollens: Suppose that $p \to q \equiv T$ and $\neg q \equiv T$. Then $q \equiv F$, and therefore, we must have $p \equiv F$. So, $\neg p \equiv T$.

Disjunctive Syllogism: Suppose that $p \vee q \equiv T$ and $\neg p \equiv T$. Then $p \equiv F$, and therefore, we must have $q \equiv T$.

Hypothetical Syllogism: Suppose that $p \to q \equiv T$ and $q \to r \equiv T$. If $p \equiv T$, then since $p \to q \equiv T$, we must have $q \equiv T$. Since $q \to r \equiv T$, we must have $r \equiv T$. Since $p \equiv T$ and $r \equiv T$, we have $p \to r \equiv T$. If $p \equiv F$, then $p \to r \equiv T$.

Conjunctive Introduction	Disjunctive Introduction	Biconditional Introduction	Constructive Dilemma
p	p	$p \to q$	$p \to q$
q	$p \vee q$	$q \to p$	$r \to s$
$p \wedge q$		$p \leftrightarrow q$	$p \vee r$
			$q \vee s$

Conjunctive Introduction: Suppose that $p \equiv T$ and $q \equiv T$. Then $p \wedge q \equiv T$.

Disjunctive Introduction: Suppose that $p \equiv T$. Then $p \vee q \equiv T$.

Biconditional Introduction: Suppose that $p \to q \equiv T$ and $q \to p \equiv T$. If $p \equiv T$, then since $p \to q \equiv T$, we must have $q \equiv T$. Since $p \equiv T$ and $q \equiv T$, we have $p \leftrightarrow q \equiv T$. If $p \equiv F$, then since $q \to p \equiv T$, we must have $q \equiv F$. Since $p \equiv F$ and $q \equiv F$, we have $p \leftrightarrow q \equiv T$.

Constructive Dilemma: Suppose that $p \to q \equiv T$, $r \to s \equiv T$, and $p \vee r \equiv T$. If $q \equiv F$ and $s \equiv F$, then since $p \to q \equiv T$, we must have $p \equiv F$. Since $r \to s \equiv T$, we must have $r \equiv F$. But then $p \vee r \equiv F$. So, there is no truth assignment satisfying $p \to q$, $r \to s$, and $p \vee r$ that will make $q \vee s \equiv F$.

Conjunctive Elimination	Disjunctive Resolution	Biconditional Elimination	Destructive Dilemma
$p \wedge q$	$p \vee q$	$p \leftrightarrow q$	$p \to q$
p	$\neg p \vee r$	$p \to q$	$r \to s$
	$q \vee r$		$\neg q \vee \neg s$
			$\neg p \vee \neg r$

Conjunctive Elimination: Suppose that $p \wedge q \equiv T$. Then $p \equiv T$ and $q \equiv T$. In particular, $p \equiv T$.

Disjunctive Resolution: Suppose that $p \vee q \equiv T$ and $\neg p \vee r \equiv T$. If $q \equiv F$ and $r \equiv F$, then since $p \vee q \equiv T$, we must have $p \equiv T$. Since $\neg p \vee r \equiv T$, we must have $\neg p \equiv T$. But then $p \wedge \neg p \equiv T$, which is impossible. So, there is no truth assignment satisfying $p \vee q$ and $\neg p \vee r$ that will make $q \vee r \equiv F$.

Biconditional Elimination: Suppose that $p \leftrightarrow q \equiv T$. If $p \to q \equiv F$, then $p \equiv T$ and $q \equiv F$. But then $p \leftrightarrow q \equiv F$. So, there is no truth assignment satisfying $p \leftrightarrow q$ that will make $p \to q \equiv F$.

Destructive Dilemma: Suppose that $p \to q \equiv T$, $r \to s \equiv T$, and $\neg q \lor \neg s \equiv T$. If $\neg p \equiv F$ and $\neg r \equiv F$, then $p \equiv T$ and $r \equiv T$. Since $p \to q \equiv T$, we must have $q \equiv T$. Since $r \to s \equiv T$, we must have $s \equiv T$. Then $\neg q \equiv F$ and $\neg s \equiv F$. Thus, $\neg q \lor \neg s \equiv F$. So, there is no truth assignment satisfying $p \to q$, $r \to s$, and $\neg q \lor \neg s$ that will make $\neg p \lor \neg r \equiv F$.

LEVEL 3

5. Let ϕ, ψ, and τ be statements. Prove each of the following:

    (i) $\phi \vdash \psi$ and $\psi \vdash \tau$ implies $\phi \vdash \tau$.

    (ii) $\phi \vdash \psi$ if and only if $\phi \to \psi$ is a tautology.

Proofs:

(i)   Let ϕ, ψ, and τ be statements with $\phi \vdash \psi$ and $\psi \vdash \tau$. Let a be a truth assignment that makes ϕ true. Since $\phi \vdash \psi$, a makes ψ true. Since $\psi \vdash \tau$, a makes τ true. Since a was an arbitrary truth assignment that makes ϕ true, $\phi \vdash \tau$. □

Notes: (1) Recall that the symbol $\vdash$ is pronounced "tautologically implies."

(2) If a truth assignment a makes a statement ϕ true, we say that a **satisfies** ϕ. If a makes ϕ false, we say that a **does not satisfy** ϕ.

(ii) Let ϕ and ψ be statements and assume that $\phi \vdash \psi$. Let a be a truth assignment of the propositional variables appearing in ϕ or ψ or both. If a satisfies ϕ, then a satisfies ψ (because $\phi \vdash \psi$). It follows that $\phi \to \psi \equiv T \to T \equiv T$. If a does not satisfy ϕ, then $\phi \to \psi \equiv F \to \psi \equiv T$. So, we have shown that every truth assignment satisfies $\phi \to \psi$. Therefore, $\phi \to \psi$ is a tautology.

Conversely, assume that $\phi \to \psi$ is a tautology, and let a be a truth assignment that satisfies ϕ. If a does not satisfy ψ, then we would have $\phi \to \psi \equiv T \to F \equiv F$. So, a must satisfy ψ. Since a was an arbitrary truth assignment that satisfies ϕ, $\phi \vdash \psi$. □

6. Let p represent a true statement. Decide if this is enough information to determine the truth value of each of the following statements. If so, state that truth value.

> (i) $p \lor q$
>
> (ii) $p \to q$
>
> (iii) $\neg p \to \neg (q \lor \neg r)$
>
> (iv) $\neg (\neg p \land q) \leftrightarrow p$
>
> (v) $(p \leftrightarrow q) \leftrightarrow \neg p$
>
> (vi) $\neg [(\neg p \land \neg q) \leftrightarrow \neg r]$
>
> (vii) $[(p \land \neg p) \to p] \land (p \lor \neg p)$
>
> (viii) $r \to [\neg q \to (\neg p \to \neg r)]$

Solutions:

(i) $(p \lor q) \equiv T \lor q \equiv$ **T**.

(ii) $p \to q \equiv T \to q$. If $q \equiv T$, we get $T \to T \equiv T$. If $q \equiv F$, we get $T \to F \equiv F$. **There is not enough information**.

(iii) $\neg p \to \neg (q \lor \neg r) \equiv F \to \neg (q \lor \neg r) \equiv$ **T**.

(iv) $\neg (\neg p \land q) \leftrightarrow p \equiv \neg (F \land q) \leftrightarrow T \equiv \neg F \leftrightarrow T \equiv T \leftrightarrow T \equiv$ **T**.

(v) $(p \leftrightarrow q) \leftrightarrow \neg p \equiv (T \leftrightarrow q) \leftrightarrow F$. If $q \equiv T$, we get $(T \leftrightarrow T) \leftrightarrow F \equiv T \leftrightarrow F \equiv F$. If $q \equiv F$, we get $(T \leftrightarrow F) \leftrightarrow F \equiv F \leftrightarrow F \equiv T$. **There is not enough information**.

(vi) $\neg [(\neg p \land \neg q) \leftrightarrow \neg r] \equiv \neg [(F \land \neg q) \leftrightarrow \neg r] \equiv \neg (F \leftrightarrow \neg r)$. If $r \equiv T$, we get $\neg T \equiv F$. If $r \equiv F$, we get $\neg F \equiv T$. **There is not enough information**.

(vii) $[(p \land \neg p) \to p] \land (p \lor \neg p) \equiv [(T \land F) \to T] \land (T \lor F) \equiv [F \to T] \land T \equiv T \land T \equiv$ **T**.

(viii) $r \to [\neg q \to (\neg p \to \neg r)] \equiv r \to [\neg q \to (F \to \neg r)] \equiv r \to [\neg q \to T] \equiv r \to T \equiv$ **T**.

LEVEL 4

7. Determine if each of the following statements is a tautology, a contradiction, or neither.

> (i) $p \land p$
>
> (ii) $p \land \neg p$
>
> (iii) $(p \lor \neg p) \to (p \land \neg p)$
>
> (iv) $\neg (p \lor q) \leftrightarrow (\neg p \land \neg q)$
>
> (v) $p \to (\neg q \land r)$
>
> (vi) $(p \leftrightarrow q) \to (p \to q)$

Solutions:

(i) If $p \equiv \text{T}$, then $p \wedge p \equiv \text{T} \wedge \text{T} \equiv \text{T}$. If $p \equiv \text{F}$, then $p \wedge p \equiv \text{F} \wedge \text{F} \equiv \text{F}$. **Neither**

(ii) $p \wedge \neg p \equiv \text{F}$. **Contradiction**

(iii) $(p \vee \neg p) \rightarrow (p \wedge \neg p) \equiv \text{T} \rightarrow \text{F} \equiv \text{F}$. **Contradiction**

(iv) Since $\neg(p \vee q) \equiv \neg p \wedge \neg q$ (De Morgan's law), $\neg(p \vee q) \leftrightarrow (\neg p \wedge \neg q)$ is a **Tautology**.

(v) If $p \equiv \text{F}$, then we have $p \rightarrow (\neg q \wedge r) \equiv \text{F} \rightarrow (\neg q \wedge r) \equiv \text{T}$. If $p \equiv \text{T}$ and $r \equiv \text{F}$, then we have $p \rightarrow (\neg q \wedge r) \equiv \text{T} \rightarrow (\neg q \wedge \text{F}) \equiv \text{T} \rightarrow \text{F} \equiv \text{F}$. **Neither**

(vi) Since $(p \leftrightarrow q) \equiv (p \rightarrow q) \wedge (q \rightarrow p)$ (by the law of the biconditional), we have that $(p \leftrightarrow q) \leftrightarrow [(p \rightarrow q) \wedge (q \rightarrow p)]$ is a tautology. In particular, $(p \leftrightarrow q) \vdash [(p \rightarrow q) \wedge (q \rightarrow p)]$. Since we also have $(p \rightarrow q) \wedge (q \rightarrow p) \vdash p \rightarrow q$, by transitivity of $\vdash$ (part (i) of Problem 5), $(p \leftrightarrow q) \vdash p \rightarrow q$. Therefore, by part (ii) of Problem 5, $(p \leftrightarrow q) \rightarrow (p \rightarrow q)$ is a **Tautology**.

8. Assume that the given compound statement is true. Determine the truth value of each propositional variable.

    (i) $p \wedge q$

    (ii) $\neg(p \rightarrow q)$

    (iii) $p \leftrightarrow [\neg(p \wedge q)]$

    (iv) $[p \wedge (q \vee r)] \wedge \neg r$

Solutions:

(i)   If $p \equiv \text{F}$ or $q \equiv \text{F}$, then $p \wedge q \equiv \text{F}$. Therefore, $\boldsymbol{p} \equiv \textbf{T}$ and $\boldsymbol{q} \equiv \textbf{T}$.

(ii)   Since $\neg(p \rightarrow q)$ is true, $p \rightarrow q$ is false. Therefore, $\boldsymbol{p} \equiv \textbf{T}$ and $\boldsymbol{q} \equiv \textbf{F}$.

(iii)   If $p \equiv \text{F}$, then $p \wedge q \equiv \text{F}$, and so $p \leftrightarrow [\neg(p \wedge q)] \equiv \text{F} \leftrightarrow \text{T} \equiv \text{F}$. So, $\boldsymbol{p} \equiv \textbf{T}$. It follows that $\neg(p \wedge q) \equiv \text{T}$, and so $p \wedge q \equiv \text{F}$. Since $p \equiv \text{T}$, we must have $\boldsymbol{q} \equiv \textbf{F}$.

(iv)   As in (i), we must have $p \wedge (q \vee r) \equiv \text{T}$ and $\neg r \equiv \text{T}$. So, $\boldsymbol{p} \equiv \textbf{T}$, $q \vee r \equiv \text{T}$, and $\boldsymbol{r} \equiv \textbf{F}$. Since $q \vee r \equiv \text{T}$ and $r \equiv \text{F}$, we must have $\boldsymbol{q} \equiv \textbf{T}$.

LEVEL 5

9. Simplify each statement.

    (i) $p \vee (p \wedge \neg p)$

    (ii) $(p \wedge q) \vee \neg p$

    (iii) $\neg p \rightarrow (\neg q \rightarrow p)$

    (iv) $(p \wedge \neg q) \vee p$

    (v) $[(q \wedge p) \vee q] \wedge [(q \vee p) \wedge p]$

Solutions:

(i) $p \vee (p \wedge \neg p) \equiv p \vee F \equiv \boldsymbol{p}$.

(ii) $(p \wedge q) \vee \neg p \equiv (p \vee \neg p) \wedge (q \vee \neg p) \equiv T \wedge (q \vee \neg p) \equiv q \vee \neg p \equiv \boldsymbol{\neg p \vee q}$.

(iii) $\neg p \rightarrow (\neg q \rightarrow p) \equiv p \vee (\neg q \rightarrow p) \equiv p \vee (q \vee p) \equiv p \vee (p \vee q) \equiv (p \vee p) \vee q \equiv \boldsymbol{p \vee q}$.

(iv) $(p \wedge \neg q) \vee p \equiv \boldsymbol{p}$ (Absorption).

(v) $[(q \wedge p) \vee q] \wedge [(q \vee p) \wedge p] \equiv [(q \wedge p) \vee q] \wedge [(p \vee q) \wedge p] \equiv q \wedge p$ (Absorption) $\equiv \boldsymbol{p \wedge q}$.

10. Determine whether each of the following logical arguments is valid or invalid. If the argument is valid, provide a deduction. If the argument is invalid, provide a counterexample.

(i)
$$\frac{\begin{array}{l} p \vee q \\ q \end{array}}{p}$$

(ii)
$$\frac{\begin{array}{l} \neg(p \wedge q) \\ q \end{array}}{\neg p}$$

(iii)
$$\frac{\begin{array}{l} \neg p \\ p \vee r \\ q \rightarrow \neg r \end{array}}{\neg q}$$

(iv)
$$\frac{\begin{array}{l} p \rightarrow q \\ r \rightarrow \neg q \end{array}}{p \rightarrow r}$$

(v) If a piano has 88 keys, then the box is empty.
If a piano does not have 88 keys, then paintings are white.
If we are in immediate danger, then the box is not empty.
Therefore, paintings are white or we are not in immediate danger.

(vi) Tangs have fangs or tings have wings.
It is not the case that tangs have fangs and tings do not have wings.
It is not the case that tangs do not have fangs and tings have wings.
Therefore, tangs have fangs and either tings have wings or tangs do not have fangs.

Solutions:

(i)   If we let $p \equiv F$ and $q \equiv T$, then $p \vee q \equiv F \vee T \equiv T$. So, we have found a truth assignment that makes the premises true and the conclusion false. Therefore, the argument is **invalid**.

(ii)   Here is a derivation.

1	$\neg(p \wedge q)$	Premise
2	q	Premise
3	$\neg p \vee \neg q$	De Morgan's law (1)
4	$\neg(\neg q)$	Law of double negation (2)
5	$\neg p$	Disjunctive syllogism (3, 4)

Therefore, the argument is **valid**.

58

(iii) Here is a derivation.

$$
\begin{array}{rll}
1 & \neg p & \text{Premise} \\
2 & p \lor r & \text{Premise} \\
3 & q \to \neg r & \text{Premise} \\
\hline
4 & r & \text{Disjunctive syllogism (2, 1)} \\
5 & \neg(\neg r) & \text{Law of double negation (4)} \\
6 & \neg q & \text{Modus tollens (3, 5)}
\end{array}
$$

Therefore, the argument is **valid**.

(iv) If we let $p \equiv T$, $q \equiv T$ and $r \equiv F$, then $p \to q \equiv T \to T \equiv T$, $r \to \neg q \equiv F \to F \equiv T$, and $p \to r \equiv T \to F \equiv F$. So, we have found a truth assignment that makes the premises true and the conclusion false. Therefore, the argument is **invalid**.

(v) Let p represent "A piano has 88 keys," let b represent "The box is empty," let w represent "Paintings are white," and let d represent "We are in immediate danger." We now give a deduction showing that the argument is valid.

$$
\begin{array}{rll}
1 & p \to b & \text{Premise} \\
2 & \neg p \to w & \text{Premise} \\
3 & d \to \neg b & \text{Premise} \\
\hline
4 & \neg w \to \neg(\neg p) & \text{Law of the contrapositive (2)} \\
5 & \neg w \to p & \text{Law of double negation (4)} \\
6 & \neg w \to b & \text{Hypothetical syllogism (5, 1)} \\
7 & \neg(\neg b) \to \neg d & \text{Law of the contrapositive (3)} \\
8 & b \to \neg d & \text{Law of double negation (7)} \\
9 & \neg w \to \neg d & \text{Hypothetical syllogism (6, 8)} \\
10 & \neg(\neg w) \lor \neg d & \text{Law of the conditional (9)} \\
11 & w \lor \neg d & \text{Law of double negation (10)}
\end{array}
$$

Therefore, the argument is **valid**.

(vi) Let f represent "Tangs have fangs," let w represent "Tings have wings." We now give a deduction showing that the argument is valid.

1	$t \lor w$	Premise
2	$\neg(t \land \neg w)$	Premise
3	$\neg(\neg t \land w)$	Premise
4	$\neg t \lor \neg(\neg w)$	De Morgan's law (2)
5	$\neg t \lor w$	Law of double negation (4)
6	$w \lor w$	Disjunctive resolution (1, 5)
7	w	Redundancy law (6)
8	$w \lor \neg t$	Disjunctive introduction (7)
9	$w \lor t$	Commutative law (1)
10	$\neg(\neg t) \lor \neg w$	De Morgan's law (3)
11	$t \lor \neg w$	Law of double negation (10)
12	$\neg w \lor t$	Commutative law (11)
13	$t \lor t$	Disjunctive resolution (9, 12)
14	t	Redundancy law (13)
15	$t \land (w \lor \neg t)$	Conjunctive introduction (14, 8)

Therefore, the argument is **valid**.

Problem Set 10

LEVEL 1

1. Let $\mathcal{L} = \{+, \cdot, S, <, 0\}$ be the language of number theory and let ϕ be the following formula: $\big((2 \cdot (v_0 + 3)) + (1 + 0)\big) < \big((0 + 1) \cdot v_1\big) \wedge \forall v_0 (v_0 \cdot 0 = 0)$. The formula ϕ is abbreviated. Write ϕ in its unabbreviated form.

Solution:

$$\left(\left(\left(< \left(+ \left(\cdot \left(S(S(0)) \left(+ \left(v_0\, S\left(S(S(0)) \right) \right) \right) \right) \right) (+(S(0)\ 0)) \right) \cdot (+(0\ S(0))\ v_1) \right) \right) \wedge \left(\forall v_0 \left(= \left((\cdot\ (v_0\ 0))\ 0 \right) \right) \right) \right)$$

2. Let $\mathcal{L} = \{\in\}$ be the language of set theory. Determine whether each occurrence of each variable in the following formula is free or bound: $\forall v_0 \exists v_1 (v_0 \in v_1 \to v_1 = v_2) \wedge \exists v_0 \forall v_2 (v_1 \in v_2)$

Solution: The first and only occurrence of v_0 is bound. The first two occurrences of v_1 are bound and the third occurrence is free. The first occurrence of v_2 is free and the second occurrence is bound.

LEVEL 2

3. Give an example of sentences ϕ and ψ and expressions α and β in the language of set theory such that $(\phi \wedge \psi) = (\alpha \wedge \beta)$ but $\phi \neq \alpha$.

Solution: Let $\phi = \forall x(x \in x)$, $\psi = \forall y(y \in y \wedge y \in y)$, $\alpha = \forall x(x \in x) \wedge \forall y(y \in y$, $\beta = y \in y)$.

If we insist on unabbreviated versions, we let $\phi = \left(\forall x (\in (x\ x)) \right)$, $\psi = \left(\forall y \left((\in (y\ y)) \wedge (\in (y\ y)) \right) \right)$, $\alpha = \left(\forall x(\in (x\ x)) \right) \wedge (\forall y((\in (y\ y)), \beta = (\in (y\ y))))$.

4. Determine if each of the following is a logical axiom:

   (i) $\forall x \exists y (x < y) \to \exists y (y < y)$

   (ii) $\forall y \big(C(y) \to C(y) \big) \to \big(C(a) \to C(a) \big)$

   (iii) $\forall x \big(C(y) \to C(x) \big) \to \big(C(y) \to \forall x C(x) \big)$

   (iv) $\Big[\big(\forall x (S(x)) \to \forall y (S(y)) \big) \to S(z) \Big] \to \Big[\forall x (S(x)) \to \big(\forall y (S(y)) \to S(z) \big) \Big]$

Solutions:

(i)   This is **not** a logical axiom. y is **not** substitutable for x in $\exists y(x < y)$. A counterexample is given by $(\mathbb{N}, <)$. In this structure, $\forall x \exists y(x < y)$ is true, but $\exists y(y < y)$ is false.

(ii)   This **is** a logical axiom. It is a substitution axiom.

(iii) This **is** a logical axiom. It is a universal derivation axiom.

(iv) This **is** a logical axiom. It is a tautology.

LEVEL 3

5. Recall that a set of statements Σ of sentential logic **tautologically implies** a statement ϕ if and only if every truth assignment for the propositional variables in Σ and ϕ that satisfies every element of Σ also satisfies ϕ. Let Γ be an arbitrary set of first-order formulas, let $\Phi = \{\phi_1, \phi_2, \ldots, \phi_n\}$ be a set of n first-order formulas, and let ψ be a first-order formula. Suppose that Φ tautologically implies ψ and for each $k = 1, 2, \ldots, n$, $\Gamma \vdash \phi_k$. Prove that $\Gamma \vdash \psi$.

Proof: The formula $\phi_1 \to \left(\phi_2 \to (\phi_3 \to \cdots \to (\phi_n \to \psi) \cdots) \right)$ is a tautology. Therefore, it is a logical axiom. Since $\Gamma \vdash \phi_1$, by modus ponens, $\Gamma \vdash \phi_2 \to (\phi_3 \to \cdots \to (\phi_n \to \psi) \cdots)$. Since $\Gamma \vdash \phi_2$, again by modus ponens, $\Gamma \vdash \phi_3 \to \cdots \to (\phi_n \to \psi)$. Continuing in this fashion a total of n times, we finally get $\Gamma \vdash \psi$. $\qquad\square$

6. Let Λ be the set of logical axioms, let Γ be a set of first-order formulas, and let ϕ be a first-order formula. Suppose that $\Lambda \cup \Gamma$ tautologically implies ϕ. Prove that $\Gamma \vdash \phi$. (Hint: Use Problem 13 from Problem Set 9.)

Proof: Suppose that $\Gamma \cup \Lambda$ tautologically implies ϕ. Then there is a finite subset $\{\gamma_1, \ldots, \gamma_m, \lambda_1, \ldots, \lambda_n\}$ that tautologically implies ϕ. $\gamma_1 \to \left(\gamma_2 \to \left(\gamma_3 \to \cdots \to \left(\gamma_m \to \left(\lambda_1 \to (\lambda_2 \to \cdots \to (\lambda_n \to \phi))) \right) \right) \cdots \right) \right)$ is a tautology. Therefore, it is a logical axiom. As we saw in Problem 5, by applying modus ponens to this tautology $m + n$ times, we get $\Gamma \vdash \phi$. $\qquad\square$

7. Let Γ be a set of first-order formulas and let ϕ, ψ be first-order formulas. Prove each of the following:

    (i) $\Gamma \vdash \phi \to \psi$ if and only if $\Gamma \cup \{\phi\} \vdash \psi$.

    (ii) $\Gamma \cup \{\phi\} \vdash \neg\psi$ if and only if $\Gamma \cup \{\psi\} \vdash \neg\phi$.

    (iii) The following are equivalent: (a) There is a formula ϕ such that $\Gamma \vdash \phi$ and $\Gamma \vdash \neg\phi$. (b) For every formula ψ, $\Gamma \vdash \psi$.

Proofs:

    (i)   First, assume that $\Gamma \vdash \phi \to \psi$. Let $\theta_1, \theta_2, \ldots, \theta_n$ be a derivation of $\phi \to \psi$ from Γ. Then the sequence $\phi, \theta_1, \theta_2, \ldots, \theta_n, \psi$ is a derivation of ψ from $\Gamma \cup \{\phi\}$.

          Conversely, we will prove by induction that if $\Gamma \cup \{\phi\} \vdash \psi$, then $\Gamma \vdash \phi \to \psi$.

          If $\psi = \phi$, then clearly $\vdash \phi \to \psi$.

          If ψ is a logical axiom or an element of Γ, then $\Gamma \vdash \psi$ and ψ tautologically implies $\phi \to \psi$. By Problem 5, $\Gamma \vdash \phi \to \psi$.

Finally, if ψ is obtained by modus ponens from θ and $\theta \to \psi$, then by the inductive assumption, we have $\Gamma \vdash \phi \to \theta$ and $\Gamma \vdash \phi \to (\theta \to \psi)$. Since $\{\phi \to \theta, \phi \to (\theta \to \psi)\}$ tautologically implies $\phi \to \psi$, by Problem 5, $\Gamma \vdash \phi \to \psi$. $\square$

(ii) Assume that $\Gamma \cup \{\phi\} \vdash \neg\psi$. By part (i), $\Gamma \vdash \phi \to \neg\psi$. Now, $\phi \to \neg\psi$ tautologically implies $\psi \to \neg\phi$. So, by Problem 5, $\Gamma \vdash \psi \to \neg\phi$. By part (i) again, $\Gamma \cup \{\psi\} \vdash \neg\phi$.

The proof of the converse follows by symmetry, $\square$

(iii) Suppose there is a formula ϕ such that $\Gamma \vdash \phi$ and $\Gamma \vdash \neg\phi$. Let ψ be an arbitrary formula. Since $\{\phi, \neg\phi\}$ tautologically implies ψ, by Problem 5, $\Gamma \vdash \psi$.

Conversely suppose that for every formula ψ, $\Gamma \vdash \psi$. Let ϕ be any formula. Then $\neg\phi$ is also a formula. By our assumption, $\Gamma \vdash \phi$ and $\Gamma \vdash \neg\phi$. $\square$

---

8. Let Γ be a set of first-order formulas and let ϕ be a first-order formula. Suppose that $\Gamma \cup \{\phi\}$ is inconsistent. Prove that $\Gamma \vdash \neg\phi$.

Proof: Since $\Gamma \cup \{\phi\}$ is inconsistent, there is a formula ψ such that $\Gamma \cup \{\phi\} \vdash \psi$ and $\Gamma \cup \{\phi\} \vdash \neg\psi$. By part (i) of Problem 7, $\Gamma \vdash \phi \to \psi$ and $\Gamma \vdash \phi \to \neg\psi$. Since $\{\phi \to \psi, \phi \to \neg\psi\}$ tautologically implies $\neg\phi$, by Problem 5, $\Gamma \vdash \neg\phi$. $\square$

LEVEL 4

9. Prove that for any formula ϕ, $\vdash \exists x \forall y \phi \to \forall y \exists x \phi$.

Proof: By part (i) of Problem 7, it suffices to show that $\exists x \forall y \phi \vdash \forall y \exists x \phi$. By Universal Generalization, it suffices to show that $\exists x \forall y \phi \vdash \exists x \phi$. By part (ii) of Problem 7, it suffices to show that $\neg \exists x \phi \vdash \neg \exists x \forall y \phi$. By the Generalized De Morgan's Laws, it suffices to show that $\forall x \neg \phi \vdash \forall x \neg \forall y \phi$. Again, by Universal Generalization, it suffices to show that $\forall x \neg \phi \vdash \neg \forall y \phi$. By Problem 8, it suffices to show that the set $\{\forall x \neg \phi, \forall y \phi\}$ is inconsistent. Now simply observe that by Universal Elimination, $\forall x \neg \phi \vdash \neg \phi$ and $\forall x \phi \vdash \phi$. $\square$

---

10. Determine whether each of the following logical arguments is valid or invalid. A and B are unary relation symbols and a and b are constant symbols. If the argument is valid, provide a deduction. If the argument is invalid, provide a counterexample.

I
$$\frac{\exists x(A(x))}{\forall x(A(x))}$$

II
$$\frac{\forall x(A(x) \lor B(x))}{\exists x \neg A(x)} \over \exists x(B(x))$$

III
$$\frac{\forall x(A(x) \lor B(x))}{\forall x(A(x) \to C(x))} \over {\forall x(B(x) \to C(x))} \over {C(a) \land C(b)}$$

IV
$$\frac{\exists x(A(x))}{B(a)} \over \exists x(A(x) \land B(x))$$

Solutions:

I. Consider the structure $\mathfrak{A} = (X, A^{\mathfrak{A}})$, where $X = \{a, b\}$, and $A^{\mathfrak{A}}(a)$. Since $A^{\mathfrak{A}}(a)$, we have $\mathfrak{A} \models \exists x(A(x))$. Since $\mathfrak{A} \not\models A(b)$, $\mathfrak{A} \not\models \forall x A(x)$. Therefore, the argument is **invalid**.

II. Here is a derivation.

$$
\begin{array}{ll}
1 \quad \forall x\big(A(x) \lor B(x)\big) & \text{Premise} \\
2 \quad \exists x \neg A(x) & \text{Premise} \\
\hline
3 \quad \neg A(a) & \text{Existential Elimination (2)} \\
4 \quad A(a) \lor B(a) & \text{Universal Elimination (1)} \\
5 \quad B(a) & \text{Disjunctive syllogism (4, 3)} \\
6 \quad \exists x\big(B(x)\big) & \text{Existential Generalization (5)}
\end{array}
$$

Therefore, the argument is **valid**.

III.   Here is a derivation.

$$
\begin{array}{ll}
1 \quad \forall x\big(A(x) \lor B(x)\big) & \text{Premise} \\
2 \quad \forall x\big(A(x) \to C(x)\big) & \text{Premise} \\
3 \quad \forall x\big(B(x) \to C(x)\big) & \text{Premise} \\
\hline
4 \quad A(a) \lor B(a) & \text{Universal Elimination (1)} \\
5 \quad A(a) \to C(a) & \text{Universal Elimination (2)} \\
6 \quad B(a) \to C(a) & \text{Universal Elimination (3)} \\
7 \quad C(a) \lor C(a) & \text{Constructive Dilemma (5, 6, 4)} \\
8 \quad C(a) & \text{Redundancy Law (7)} \\
9 \quad A(b) \lor B(b) & \text{Universal Elimination (1)} \\
10 \quad A(b) \to C(b) & \text{Universal Elimination (2)} \\
11 \quad B(b) \to C(b) & \text{Universal Elimination (3)} \\
12 \quad C(b) \lor C(b) & \text{Constructive Dilemma (10, 11, 9)} \\
13 \quad C(b) & \text{Redundancy Law (12)} \\
14 \quad C(a) \land C(b) & \text{Conjunctive Introduction (8, 13)}
\end{array}
$$

Therefore, the argument is **valid**.

IV.   Consider the structure $\mathfrak{A} = \big(X, A^{\mathfrak{A}}, B^{\mathfrak{A}}\big)$, where $X = \{a, b\}$, $A^{\mathfrak{A}}(b)$ and $B^{\mathfrak{A}}(a)$. Since $A^{\mathfrak{A}}(b)$, $\mathfrak{A} \vDash \exists x\big(A(x)\big)$. Since $B^{\mathfrak{A}}(a)$, $\mathfrak{A} \vDash B(a)$. However, $\mathfrak{A} \nvDash \exists x\big(A(x) \land B(x)\big)$. Therefore, the argument is **invalid**.

LEVEL 5

11. Prove Unique Readability for Formulas (Theorem 10.4).

Proof: We need the analogues of Theorems 10.1 and 10.2 for formulas. The proofs are similar to the proofs of those theorems. I will leave the proof of the first to the reader and prove the second. We will prove by the principle of induction on formulas that every proper initial segment of a formula has more left than right parentheses. Let's start with an atomic formula, say $(R(t_1 t_2 \cdots t_n))$. A proper initial segment of this formula has one of the following forms:

$$($$
$$(R$$
$$(R($$
$(R(s_1, \text{ where } s_1 \text{ is a proper initial segment of } t_1$
$$(R(t_1$$
$(R(t_1 t_2 \cdots s_k, \text{ where } s_k \text{ is a proper initial segment of } t_k$
$$(R(t_1 t_2 \cdots t_k$$
$$(R(t_1 t_2 \cdots t_k)$$

It is easy to check that each of these expressions has more left than right parentheses. For example, (has 1 left parenthesis and 0 right parentheses. As another example, if s_1 has i left parentheses and j right parentheses, then by the inductive assumption, $i > j$. It follows that $(R(s_1$ has $i + 2$ left parentheses and j right parentheses, and $i + 2 > i > j$. The other six cases are similar.

Now assume that the statement "every proper initial segment of a formula has more left than right parentheses" is true for the formula ϕ.

A proper initial segment of $(\neg\phi)$ has one of the following forms:

$$($$
$$(\neg$$
$(\neg\alpha, \text{ where } \alpha \text{ is a proper initial segment of } \phi$
$$(\neg\phi$$

It is easy to check that each of these expressions has more left than right parentheses. For the third form, we need to use the inductive assumption. For the last form, we use the fact that a formula has the same number of left and right parentheses (this is the analogue of Theorem 10.1 for formulas).

Similar arguments can be made for $(\phi \wedge \psi)$, $(\phi \vee \psi)$, $(\phi \rightarrow \psi)$, $(\phi \leftrightarrow \psi)$, $(\forall x\phi)$, and $(\exists x\phi)$.

By the principle of induction on formulas, every proper initial segment of a formula has more left parentheses than right parentheses.

Now, a formula from group (i) (an atomic formula) has the form $(R(t_1 t_2 \cdots t_n))$ and a formula from group (ii) has the form $(\neg\psi)$. These two formulas cannot be the same because they disagree in the second symbol. Similar arguments can be made for formulas from different groups among (i), (ii), (iii), and (iv).

Now, suppose ϕ can be written as both $\big(R(t_1 t_2 \cdots t_n)\big)$ and $\big(S(u_1 u_2 \cdots u_n)\big)$. Since the second symbols must agree, we have $R = S$ (as symbols). Deleting the first three symbols from each expression, we now have $t_1 t_2 \cdots t_n) = u_1 u_2 \cdots u_n)$. Suppose toward contradiction that there is a positive integer k such that $t_k \neq u_k$. Let j be the least such positive integer. Then, as sequences of symbols, t_j is a proper initial segment of u_j or u_j is a proper initial segment of t_j. Without loss of generality, assume that t_j is a proper initial segment of u_j. Since u_j is a term, t_j has more left parentheses than right parentheses, contradicting the analogue of Theorem 10.1. It follows that for each $k \leq n$, we have $t_k = u_k$. Therefore, $\big(R(t_1 t_2 \cdots t_n)\big)$ and $\big(S(u_1 u_2 \cdots u_n)\big)$ are the same string of symbols.

Next, suppose that ϕ can be written as both $(\neg\psi)$ and $(\neg\theta)$. Then clearly $\psi = \theta$, so that $(\neg\psi)$ and $(\neg\theta)$ are the same string of symbols.

Next, suppose that ϕ can be written as both $(\psi C \theta)$ and $(\tau D \mu)$. Then we must have $\psi C \theta) = \tau D \mu)$. Suppose toward contradiction that $\psi \neq \tau$. Then, as sequences of symbols, ψ is a proper initial segment of τ or τ is a proper initial segment of ψ. Without loss of generality, assume that ψ is a proper initial segment of τ. Since τ is a formula, ψ has more left parentheses than right parentheses, contradicting that formulas have the same number of left and right parentheses. It follows that $\psi = \tau$. So, we have $C \theta) = D \mu)$. So, C and D must be the same symbol, and therefore, $\theta = \mu$.

The case of quantifiers can be handled similarly. $\square$

12. Let x and y be variables. Prove that if y does not occur in ϕ, then x is substitutable for y in ϕ_y^x and $\big(\phi_y^x\big)^y = \phi$. Then provide a counterexample to show that $\big(\phi_y^x\big)_x^y$ does not necessarily equal ϕ.

Proof: We first prove that for each term u, if y does not occur in u, then $\big(u_y^x\big)_x^y = u$.

If u is a variable such that $u \neq y$, then $u_y^x = \begin{cases} u & \text{if } u \neq x. \\ y & \text{if } u = x. \end{cases}$ So, $\big(u_y^x\big)_x^y = \begin{cases} u & \text{if } u \neq x \\ x & \text{if } u = x \end{cases} = u.$

If u is a constant symbol, then $u \neq x$ and $u \neq y$. So, $\big(u_y^x\big)_x^y = u_x^y = u.$

Suppose that $\big(u_{i_y}^x\big)_x^y = u_i$ for each $i = 1, 2, \ldots, n$ and that u is $\big(f(u_1 u_2 \cdots u_n)\big)$. Then $\big(u_y^x\big)_x^y$ is $\left(f\left(\big(u_{1_y}^x\big)_x^y \big(u_{2_y}^x\big)_x^y \cdots \big(u_{n_y}^x\big)_x^y\right)\right) = \big(f(u_1 u_2 \cdots u_n)\big).$

By the principle of induction on terms, for each term u, if y does not occur in u, then $\big(u_y^x\big)_x^y = u.$

We now prove that for each formula ϕ, if y does not occur in ϕ, then $\big(\phi_y^x\big)_x^y = \phi$.

If ϕ is the atomic formula $\big(R(u_1 u_2 \cdots u_n)\big)$, then ϕ_y^x is the atomic formula $\left(R\left(u_{1_y}^x u_{2_y}^x \cdots u_{n_y}^x\right)\right)$, x is substitutable for y in ϕ_y^x and $\big(\phi_y^x\big)_x^y = \left(R\left(\big(u_{1_y}^x\big)_x^y \big(u_{2_y}^x\big)_x^y \cdots \big(u_{n_y}^x\big)_x^y\right)\right) = \big(R(u_1 u_2 \cdots u_n)\big) = \phi.$

66

If ϕ is $\neg\psi$, where x is substitutable for y in ψ_y^x and $\left(\psi_y^x\right)_x^y = \psi$, then $\phi_y^x = \neg\psi_y^x$. So, x is substitutable for y in ϕ_y^x and $\left(\phi_y^x\right)_x^y = \neg\left(\psi_y^x\right)_x^y = \neg\psi = \phi$.

If ϕ is $\psi \wedge \theta$, where x is substitutable for y in ψ_y^x and θ_y^x, and $\left(\psi_y^x\right)_x^y = \psi$ and $\left(\theta_y^x\right)_x^y = \theta$, then $\phi_y^x = \psi_y^x \wedge \theta_y^x$. So, x is substitutable for y in ϕ_y^x and $\left(\phi_y^x\right)_x^y = \left(\psi_y^x\right)_x^y \wedge \left(\theta_y^x\right)_x^y = \psi \wedge \theta = \phi$.

The arguments for $\psi \vee \theta$, $\psi \to \theta$, and $\psi \leftrightarrow \theta$ are similar.

Suppose that ϕ is $\forall z\psi$, where x is substitutable for y in ψ_y^x and $\left(\psi_y^x\right)_x^y = \psi$. There are two cases to consider.

<u>Case 1</u> ($z = x$): $\phi_y^x = (\forall z\psi)_y^x = \forall x\psi_y^x = \forall x\psi$. Since y does not occur free in $\forall x\psi$ (in fact, y does not occur in $\forall x\psi$), x is substitutable for y in $\forall x\psi = \phi_y^x$ and $\left(\phi_y^x\right)_x^y = (\forall x\psi)_x^y = \forall x\psi_x^y = \forall x\psi = \phi$.

<u>Case 2</u> ($z \neq x$): $\phi_y^x = (\forall z\psi)_y^x = \forall z\psi_y^x$. Since $x \neq y$ and x is substitutable for y in ψ_y^x, x is substitutable for y in $\forall z\psi_y^x = \phi_y^x$. Also, $\left(\phi_y^x\right)_x^y = \left(\forall z\psi_y^x\right)_x^y = \forall z\left(\psi_y^x\right)_x^y = \forall z\psi = \phi$.

By the principle of induction on formulas, for each formula ϕ, if y does not occur in ϕ, then x is substitutable for y in ϕ_y^x and $\left(\phi_y^x\right)_x^y = \phi$.

Now, let ϕ be the formula $\forall x(x < y)$. Then $\phi_y^x = \phi = \forall x(x < y)$ and $\left(\phi_y^x\right)_x^y = \forall x(x < x)$. So, we see that $\left(\phi_y^x\right)_x^y \neq \phi$. $\qquad\square$

Problem Set 11

LEVEL 1

1. Prove from the axioms of ZF that for all $n \geq 2$, every n-tuple of n sets is a set.

Proof: We prove by induction that for $n \in \mathbb{N}$ with $n \geq 2$ that every n-tuple of n sets is a set.

Base Case ($k = 2$): The base case was done in part 4 of Example 11.1.

Inductive Step: Assume that every k-tuple of k sets is a set and let $x_1, x_2, \ldots, x_k, x_{k+1}$ be sets. By the inductive hypothesis, $x = (x_1, x_2, \ldots x_k)$ is a set. By part 4 of Example 11.1, (x, x_{k+1}) is a set. Therefore, $(x_1, x_2, \ldots, x_k, x_{k+1}) = \big((x_1, x_2, \ldots, x_k), x_{k+1}\big) = (x, x_{k+1})$ is a set.

By the Principle of Mathematical Induction, for all $n \in \mathbb{N}$ with $n \geq 2$, every n-tuple of n sets is a set. $\square$

2. Prove that Zorn's Lemma is equivalent to the following statement: Let $(P, \leq)$ be a poset with nonempty domain such that each chain in P with nonempty domain has an upper bound in P. Then P contains at least one maximal element.

Proof: First assume that Zorn's Lemma holds and let $(P, \leq)$ be a poset with nonempty domain such that each chain in P with nonempty domain has an upper bound in P. Consider the empty chain, $(\emptyset, \leq)$. Since $P \neq \emptyset$, there is $a \in P$. The statement $\forall x \in \emptyset (x \leq a)$ is vacuously true. Therefore, a is an upper bound of $(\emptyset, \leq)$. By Zorn's Lemma, P contains at least one maximal element.

Next assume that the given statement holds and let $(P, \leq)$ be a poset such that each chain in P has an upper bound in P. Then P must be nonempty. Since each chain in P has an upper bound in P, it follows that each chain in P with nonempty domain has an upper bound in P. The given statement then implies that P contains at least one maximal element. $\square$

LEVEL 2

3. Prove from the axioms of ZF that the cartesian product of two sets is a set.

Proof: Let A and B be sets. By the pairing axiom, $\{A, B\}$ is a set. So, by the union axiom, $A \cup B = \bigcup\{A, B\}$ is a set. By applying the power set axiom twice, we see that $\mathcal{P}\big(\mathcal{P}(A \cup B)\big)$ is a set. If $a \in A$ and $b \in B$, then $\{a\}$ and $\{a, b\}$ are in $\mathcal{P}(A \cup B)$. So, $(a, b) = \{\{a\}, \{a, b\}\} \in \mathcal{P}\big(\mathcal{P}(A \cup B)\big)$. By Bounded Comprehension, $A \times B = \big\{x \in \mathcal{P}\big(\mathcal{P}(A \cup B)\big) \mid x = (a, b) \wedge a \in A \wedge b \in B\big\}$ is a set. $\square$

4. Prove that Zorn's Lemma is equivalent to the following statement: If X is a set of sets such that, for each $Y \subseteq X$ such that $(Y, \subseteq)$ is a linearly ordered set, $\bigcup Y \in X$, then $(X, \subseteq)$ has at least one maximal element.

Proof: First assume that Zorn's Lemma holds and let X be a set of sets such that, for each $Y \subseteq X$ that is linearly ordered by $\subseteq$, $\bigcup Y \subseteq X$. Since $X \subseteq \mathcal{P}(\bigcup X)$, by part 2 of Example 11.6, $(X, \subseteq)$ is a partially ordered set (if $A \subseteq B$ and $(B, \leq)$ is a partially ordered set, then $(A, \leq)$ is a partially ordered set). Let $(C, \subseteq)$ be a chain in X. Then $C \subseteq X$ and therefore, $\bigcup C \in X$. So, $\bigcup C$ is an upper bound of $(C, \subseteq)$ in X. By Zorn's Lemma, $(X, \subseteq)$ has at least one maximal element.

Next assume that the given statement holds and let $(P, \leq)$ be a poset such that each chain in P has an upper bound in P. Let $X = \{C \subseteq P \mid (C, \leq) \text{ is a chain in } P\}$. Then X is a set of sets. Let $Y \subseteq X$ be such that $(Y \subseteq)$ is a linearly ordered set. It is straightforward to check that $\bigcup Y$ is a linearly ordered set. So, $\bigcup Y \in X$. The given statement implies that $(X, \subseteq)$ has a maximal element, let's call it D. Since $(D, \leq)$ is a chain, D has an upper bound s. Suppose toward contradiction that s is not a maximal element of $(P, \leq)$. Then there is $y \in P$ with $s < y$. It follows that $(D \cup \{y\}, \leq)$ is a chain in P, contradicting the maximality of D. $\quad\square$

LEVEL 3

Proof: First assume that (i) holds. Let X be a set of nonempty pairwise disjoint sets and let $f : X \to \bigcup X$ be such that for each $x \in X$, $f(x) \in x$. Since X is a set, by the union axiom, $\bigcup X$ is a set. By bounded comprehension, $Y = \{y \in \bigcup X \mid \exists x(x \in X \wedge y = f(x))\}$ is a set. For each $x \in X$, $f(x) \in x$ and $f(x) \in Y$. So, each set in X has an element in Y. Suppose $x \in X$ and $y \in Y$ with $y \in x$. If $f(z) = y$, then $y \in z$. Since X is pairwise disjoint, $z = x$. So, $f(z) = f(x)$. Therefore, $f(x)$ is the only element of Y that is in x.

Now, assume that (ii) holds and let X be a set of nonempty sets. For each $x \in X$, $\{x\}$ is a set by the pairing axiom. By Problem 3, for each $x \in X$, $x \times \{x\}$ is a set. By replacement, $A = \{x \times \{x\} \mid x \in X\}$ is a set. Also, if $x \times \{x\}, y \times \{y\} \in A$ with $z \in (x \times \{x\}) \cap (y \times \{y\})$, then there are $j \in x$ and $k \in y$ with $z = (j, x)$ and $z = (k, y)$. So, $(j, x) = (k, y)$, and thus, $x = y$. Therefore, $x \times \{x\} = y \times \{y\}$, showing that A is a set of nonempty pairwise disjoint sets. By (ii), there is a set Y containing exactly one element from each set in A. Let $f = \{(a, b) \mid a \in X \wedge (b, a) \in Y\}$. Let's check that $f : X \to \bigcup X$. If $a \in X$, then $a \times \{a\} \in A$. So, there is exactly one element of $a \times \{a\}$ in Y, say (b, a). Since $a \in X$ and $(b, a) \in Y$, $(a, b) \in f$. Also, since $(b, a) \in a \times \{a\}$, $b \in a$. Since $a \in X$ and $b \in a$, we have $b \in \bigcup X$. If $(a, b), (a, b') \in f$, then we have $a \in X$ and $(b, a), (b', a) \in Y$. Since $(b, a), (b', a) \in a \times \{a\}$ and Y contains exactly one element from each set in A, $b = b'$. This shows that f is a function. Finally, let $a \in X$. Then $(f(a), a) \in Y$. So, we have $(f(a), a) \in a \times \{a\}$. Therefore, $f(a) \in a$. $\quad\square$

Proof: First assume that Zorn's Lemma holds and let X be a set of sets with finite character. Let $(C, \subseteq)$ be a chain in X and let $Y = \bigcup C$. If A is a finite subset of Y, then $A \in X$ (because X has finite character). Since X has finite character, $Y \in X$. Therefore, Y is an upper bound of $(C, \subseteq)$ in X. By Zorn's Lemma, $(X, \subseteq)$ has at least one maximal element.

Next assume that Tukey's Lemma holds and let $(P, \leq)$ be a poset such that each chain in P has an upper bound in P. Let $X = \{C \subseteq P \mid (C, \leq) \text{ is a chain in } P\}$. If $A \in X$ and B is a finite subset of X, then $B \in X$ because a subset of a chain is a chain. If $A \notin X$, then A is not a chain. So, there are incomparable elements $a, b \in A$. Then the finite subset $\{a, b\}$ of A is not in X. Therefore, X has finite character. By Tukey's lemma, $(X, \subseteq)$ has a maximal element, let's call it D. Since $(D, \leq)$ is a chain, D has an upper bound s. Suppose toward contradiction that s is not a maximal element of $(P, \leq)$. Then there is $y \in P$ with $s < y$. It follows that $(D \cup \{y\}, \leq)$ is a chain in P, contradicting the maximality of D. $\qquad\square$

LEVEL 4

> 7. Prove that the bounded comprehension schema follows from the replacement schema.

Proof: Let $b_1, b_2, \ldots, b_n, a$ be sets and let ϕ be a first-order formula with free variables $w, y_1, y_2, \ldots, y_n, x$. Let $\psi(u, v, y_1, y_2, \ldots, y_n, x)$ be the formula

$$\phi(u, y_1, y_2, \ldots, y_n, x) \wedge v = u.$$

Suppose that $\psi(u, w, y_1, y_2, \ldots, y_n, x) \wedge \psi(u, v, y_1, y_2, \ldots, y_n, x)$. Then $w = u$ and $v = u$. So, $w = v$. Therefore, we have

$$\forall u \forall w \forall v \forall y_1 \forall y_2 \cdots \forall y_n \forall x \left(\big(\phi(u, w, y_1, y_2, \ldots, y_n, x) \wedge \phi(u, v, y_1, y_2, \ldots, y_n, x) \big) \rightarrow w = v \right).$$

By the replacement schema, $\exists z \forall v \left(v \in z \leftrightarrow \exists u \big(u \in a \wedge \psi(u, v, b_1, b_2, \ldots, b_n, a) \big) \right)$.

Let $z = \{ v \mid \exists u \big(u \in a \wedge \psi(u, v, b_1, b_2, \ldots, b_n, a) \big) \}$.

Now, $\psi(u, v, b_1, b_2, \ldots, b_n, a)$ is equivalent to $\phi(u, b_1, b_2, \ldots, b_n, a) \wedge v = u$.

Therefore, $u \in a \wedge \psi(u, v, b_1, b_2, \ldots, b_n, a)$ is equivalent to $u \in a \wedge \phi(u, b_1, b_2, \ldots, b_n, a) \wedge v = u$.

Let $z' = \{ v \mid v \in a \wedge \phi(v, b_1, b_2, \ldots, b_n, a) \}$. We will now show that $z = z'$.

First, let $v \in z'$. Then $v \in a$ and $\phi(v, b_1, b_2, \ldots, b_n, a)$. Therefore, there is a u such that $u \in a$ and $\phi(u, b_1, b_2, \ldots, b_n, a)$ and $v = u$. So, $v \in z$. Therefore, $z' \subseteq z$.

Now, let $v \in z$. Then there is a u such that $u \in a$, $\phi(u, b_1, b_2, \ldots, b_n, a)$, and $v = u$. So, $v \in a$ and $\phi(v, b_1, b_2, \ldots, b_n, a)$. Thus, $v \in z'$. Therefore, $z \subseteq z'$.

Since $z' \subseteq z$ and $z \subseteq z'$, we have $z = z'$, completing the proof. $\qquad\square$

8. Let $\tau(n)$ be the formula $\phi(n) \wedge \psi(n)$, where

$$\phi(n) \equiv \forall m(m \notin n) \vee \exists k \forall m\big(m \in n \leftrightarrow (m \in k \vee m = k)\big)$$

and

$$\psi(n) \equiv \forall k \left(k \in n \rightarrow \Big(\forall m(m \notin k) \vee \exists m\big(m \in n \wedge \forall j(j \in k \leftrightarrow (j \in m \vee j = m))\big)\Big)\right)$$

Use the axiom of infinity, the bounded comprehension schema, and the axiom of foundation to prove that $\{n \mid \tau(n)\}$ is the set of natural numbers. Then prove that if there is a set x such that $x = \{x\}$, then $\{n \mid \tau(n)\}$ is **not** the set of natural numbers.

Proof: Let $A = \{n \mid \tau(n)\}$. We first prove by induction on $n \in \omega$ that $\omega \subseteq A$. 0 satisfies $\forall m(m \notin n)$, and therefore $\phi(0)$ is true. Also, $\psi(0)$ is vacuously true. So, $\tau(0)$ is true. Therefore, $0 \in A$. Now assume $k \in A$. Then $k + 1 = k \cup \{k\}$. So, $\forall m\big(m \in k + 1 \leftrightarrow (m \in k \vee m = k)\big)$. So, $\phi(k + 1)$ is true. We need to show that $\psi(k + 1)$ is true. Let $t \in k + 1$. Then $t \in k$ or $t = k$. If $t \in k$, then since $\psi(k)$ is true (by induction), we have $\forall m(m \notin t) \vee \exists m\big(m \in k \wedge \forall j(j \in t \leftrightarrow (j \in m \vee j = m))\big)$. Since $k \subseteq k + 1$, $m \in k$ implies $m \in k + 1$. So, we have $\forall m(m \notin t) \vee \exists m\big(m \in k + 1 \wedge \forall j(j \in t \leftrightarrow (j \in m \vee j = m))\big)$. If $t = k$, then since $\phi(k)$ is true (by induction), $\forall m(m \notin k) \vee \exists j \forall m\big(m \in k \leftrightarrow (m \in j \vee m = j)\big)$. If $\forall m(m \notin k)$ holds, then $\psi(k + 1)$ is true. If $\forall m(m \notin k)$ does not hold, then $k - 1 \in k$ and we have $\forall j\big(j \in k \leftrightarrow (j \in k - 1 \vee j = k - 1)\big)$. Since $k \subseteq k + 1$, $k - 1 \in k + 1$. It follows that we have $\exists m\big(m \in k + 1 \wedge \forall j(j \in k \leftrightarrow (j \in m \vee j = m))\big)$ (namely, $m = k - 1$). Therefore, once again, $\psi(k + 1)$ is true. Since $\phi(k + 1)$ is true and $\psi(k + 1)$ is true, $\tau(k + 1)$ is true, and $k + 1 \in A$. By the Principle of Mathematical Induction, $\omega \subseteq A$.

We now prove that $A \subseteq \omega$. Suppose that there is $x \in A$ such that $x \notin \omega$. We inductively define a sequence $x_0, x_1, \ldots, x_n, \ldots$ such that $x_0 = x$ and for all $n \in \omega$, $x_n \in A \setminus \omega$ and $x_{n+1} \in x_n$. Assuming x_n has been defined, first note that $x_n \neq \emptyset$ because $\emptyset = 0 \in \omega$. Therefore, since $\phi(x_n)$ is true, $\exists k \forall m\big(m \in x_n \leftrightarrow (m \in k \vee m = k)\big)$. In other words, there is a set k such that $x_n = k \cup \{k\}$. Let $x_{n+1} = k$. Then $\tau(x_{n+1})$ is true, and so, $x_{n+1} \in A$. If $x_{n+1} \in \omega$, then $x_n = x_{n+1} \cup \{x_{n+1}\} \in \omega$, which it is not. So, $x_{n+1} \notin \omega$.

The set $\{x_n \mid n \in \omega\}$ has no $\in$-least element, contradicting the axiom of foundation. It follows that there is no $x \in A$ such that $x \notin \omega$. So, $A \subseteq \omega$.

Since $\omega \subseteq A$ and $A \subseteq \omega$, $\{n \mid \tau(n)\} = A = \omega$.

Now, suppose that x satisfies $x = \{x\}$. Then $x \cup \{x\} = x \cup x = x$. Since x is the only element of x, we see that $x \in A$. We now show by induction that for all $n \in \omega$, $x \neq n$. Since $x \in x$ and $\emptyset$ has no elements, $x \neq \emptyset = 0$. Assume that $x \neq k$. If $k + 1 = x$, then $k \cup \{k\} = x$. So, $k \in x$. But the only element of x is x. So, $x = k$, contradicting our assumption that $x \neq k$. By the Principle of Mathematical Induction, for all $n \in \omega$, $x \neq n$. Thus, $x \notin \omega$. Therefore, $A \neq \omega$. $\square$

9. Prove that the set of natural numbers exists using only the axiom of infinity and the bounded comprehension schema.

Proof: By the axiom of infinity, there is a set x such that $\emptyset \in x \land \forall y(y \in x \to y \cup \{y\} \in x)$. By the bounded comprehension schema, we can define the set $A = \bigcap\{z \in \mathcal{P}(x) \mid \phi(z)\}$, where $\phi(z)$ is the formula $\emptyset \in z \land \forall k(k \in z \to k \cup \{k\} \in z)$.

Recall from Lesson 5 that the set of natural numbers, ω is defined to be the unique set satisfying (i) $\emptyset \in \omega$, (ii) $n \in \omega$ implies $n^+ \in \omega$, and (iii) if X is any set satisfying (i) and (ii), then $\omega \subseteq X$.

We now show that A is the unique set satisfying (i), (ii), and (iii) above.

Let $z \in \mathcal{P}(x)$ with $\phi(z)$ true. Then $\emptyset \in z$. Since $z \in \mathcal{P}(x)$ was an arbitrary element satisfying $\phi(z)$, $\emptyset \in A$. So, (i) holds.

Let $n \in A$ and let $z \in \mathcal{P}(x)$ such that $\phi(z)$. Then $n \in z$. Since $\phi(z)$ and $n \in z$, $n^+ \in z$. Since $z \in \mathcal{P}(x)$ with $\phi(z)$ was arbitrary, $n^+ \in A$. So, (ii) holds.

Let X be a set satisfying (i) and (ii). Then $\phi(X)$ holds. So, $\phi(x \cap X)$ holds. Since $x \cap X \subseteq x$, we have $x \cap X \in \mathcal{P}(x)$, and so, $A \subseteq x \cap X$. Since $x \cap X \subseteq X$, we have $A \subseteq X$. Therefore, (iii) holds.

So, A is a set satisfying (i), (ii), and (iii).

If B also satisfies (i), (ii), and (iii), then by (iii), we have $A \subseteq B$ and $B \subseteq A$. Thus, $A = B$. This shows that A is the unique set satisfying (i), (ii), and (iii).

So, A is the set of natural numbers. $\qquad\qquad\square$

10. Prove that for every partially ordered set $(P, \leq_P)$, there is a linearly ordered set $(P, \leq_L)$ such that $\leq_P \subseteq \leq_L$.

Proof: Let $(P, \leq)$ be a partially ordered set and define X as follows:

$$X = \{(K, \leq_K) \mid K \subseteq P \land (K, \leq_K) \text{ is a linearly ordered set} \land \forall x, y \in K(x \leq_P y \to x \leq_K y)\}$$

$(X, \subseteq)$ is a partially ordered set. Let $(C, \subseteq)$ be a chain in X. Then $\bigcup C \in X$. So, $\bigcup C$ is an upper bound of $(C, \subseteq)$ in X. By Zorn's Lemma, $(X, \subseteq)$ has at least one maximal element, say $(L, \leq_L)$. Suppose toward contradiction that $L \neq P$. Let $x \in P \setminus L$, let $M = L \cup \{x\}$, and let

$$\leq_M = \leq_L \cup \{(x, y) \mid y \in L \land \exists z \in L(x \leq_P z \land z \leq_L y)\}$$
$$\cup \{(y, x) \mid \neg(y \in L \land \exists z \in L(x \leq_P z \land z \leq_L y))\}.$$

Then $(M, \leq_M)$ is a linearly ordered set, contradicting the maximality of $(L, \leq_L)$. So $L = P$ and $(P, \leq_L)$ is a linearly ordered set such that $\leq_P \subseteq \leq_L$. $\qquad\square$

Problem Set 12

LEVEL 1

1. Prove each of the following or provide a counterexample:

   (i) Every transitive set is an ordinal.

   (ii) Every set that is well-ordered by $\in$ is an ordinal.

Solutions:

(i) $\mathcal{P}(\{0,1\}) = \mathcal{P}(\{\emptyset, \{\emptyset\}\}) = \{\emptyset, \{\emptyset\}, \{\{\emptyset\}\}, \{\emptyset, \{\emptyset\}\}\}$ is transitive by part 5 of Example 12.1. However, this set is **not** linearly ordered because $\{\{\emptyset\}\}$ and $\{\emptyset, \{\emptyset\}\}$ are incomparable (neither is an element of the other). Therefore, $\mathcal{P}(\{0,1\})$ is a transitive set that is **not** an ordinal.

(ii) $\{0, 2\} = \{\emptyset, \{\emptyset, \{\emptyset\}\}\}$ is well-ordered by $\in$ because it is a subset of the well-ordered set $3 = \{0, 1, 2\}$. However, this set is **not** transitive because $\{\emptyset\} \in \{\emptyset, \{\emptyset\}\} \in \{\emptyset, \{\emptyset, \{\emptyset\}\}\}$, but $\{\emptyset\} \notin \{\emptyset, \{\emptyset, \{\emptyset\}\}\}$ (or equivalently, $1 \in 2 \in \{0, 2\}$, but $1 \notin \{0, 2\}$). Therefore, $\{0, 2\}$ is a set that is well-ordered by $\in$ that is **not** an ordinal.

2. Let α, β, and γ be ordinals with $\alpha \in \beta$ and $\beta \in \gamma$. Prove that $\alpha \in \gamma$.

Proof: Since γ is an ordinal, γ is transitive. Therefore, $\beta \in \gamma$ and $\alpha \in \beta$ implies that $\alpha \in \gamma$. $\qquad\square$

LEVEL 2

3. Strong Transfinite Induction is the following statement:

   If S is a subclass of **ON** such that for all $\alpha \in$ **ON**, $\forall \beta < \alpha \ (\beta \in S) \to \alpha \in S$, then $S =$ **ON**.

   Use Theorem 12.10 (Ordinal Well Ordering Principle) to prove Strong Transfinite Induction.

Proof: Let S be a subclass of **ON** such that for all $\alpha \in$ **ON**, $\forall \beta < \alpha \ (\beta \in S) \to \alpha \in S$. Assume towards contradiction that $S \neq$ **ON**. Let $A = \{\alpha \in \textbf{ON} \mid \alpha \notin S\}$ (so, A is the class of ordinals **not** in S). Since $S \neq$ **ON**, A is nonempty. So, by the Ordinal Well Ordering Principle, A has an $\in$-least element, let's call it α. Since α is the $\in$-least element of A, $\forall \beta < \alpha \ (\beta \in A)$ is false. Therefore, $\forall \beta < \alpha \ (\beta \in S)$ is true. Thus, $\alpha \in S$, contradicting that $\alpha \in A$. So, $S =$ **ON**. $\qquad\square$

4. Prove that each natural number is well-ordered by $\in$, and use this to conclude that each natural number is an ordinal.

Proof: We prove by induction on $n \in \omega$ that each natural number is well-ordered by $\in$. 0 is trivially well-ordered by $\in$ because it has no elements and no non-empty subsets. Suppose that $k \in \omega$ is well-ordered by $\in$. We will show that $k + 1 = k \cup \{k\}$ is well-ordered by $\in$.

To see that $\in$ is antireflexive on $k + 1$, let $j \in k + 1$. Then $j \in k$ or $j = k$. If $j \in k$, then since $\in$ is antireflexive on k, $j \notin j$. If $j = k$, then $j \notin j$ because if $j \in j$, then j would be an element of k with $j \in j$, contradicting that k is antireflexive.

To see that $\in$ is antisymmetric on $k + 1$, let $j, t \in k + 1$. If $j, t \in k$, then since $\in$ is antireflexive on k, we have $j \in t$ and $t \in j$ implies $t = j$. Suppose that $j = k$ or $t = k$. Without loss of generality, let $j = k$. If $j \in t$ and $t \in j$, then since $j = k$ is a transitive set (by part 6 of Example 12.1), $k \in k$. As in the last paragraph, this is a contradiction.

To see that $\in$ is transitive on $k + 1$, let $j, t, u \in k + 1$, and suppose that $j \in t$ and $t \in u$. If $u = k$, then since k is a transitive set (again by part 6 of Example 12.1), $j \in k = u$. If $u \in k$, then again, since k is a transitive set, $t \in k$ and $j \in k$. Since $\in$ is transitive on k (by the inductive hypothesis), we have $j \in u$.

To see that $(k + 1, \in)$ satisfies trichotomy, let $j, t \in k + 1$ and assume that $j \notin t$ and $t \notin j$. If $t = k$, then since $j \notin t$, $j = k = t$. Similarly, if $j = k$, then since $t \notin j$, $t = k = j$. If $t \neq k$ and $j \neq k$, then $t, j \in k$. Since $(k, \in)$ satisfies trichotomy, (by the inductive hypothesis) $t = j$. So, $(k + 1, \in)$ satisfies trichotomy.

Finally, let A be a nonempty subset of $k + 1$. If $A \setminus \{k\} \neq \emptyset$, then $A \setminus \{k\} \subseteq k$. Since k is well-ordered by $\in$ (by the inductive hypothesis), $A \setminus \{k\}$ has an $\in$-least element, say j. Since $j \in k$, j is the $\in$-least element of A. If $A \setminus \{k\} = \emptyset$, then k is the only element of A, and therefore, it is the $\in$-least element of A. Therefore, $k + 1$ is well-ordered by $\in$.

Since each natural number is transitive (by part 6 of Example 12.1) and well-ordered by $\in$, each natural number is an ordinal. $\qquad\square$

LEVEL 3

5. Let α be an ordinal. Prove each of the following:

    (i) $\alpha + 1 = \alpha \cup \{\alpha\}$ is also an ordinal.

    (ii)   If $x \in \alpha$, then x is an ordinal and $x = \text{pred}(\alpha, x)$.

Proofs:

    (i)   We first show that $\alpha + 1$ is transitive. Let $\beta \in \alpha + 1$ and let $\gamma \in \beta$. Then $\beta \in \alpha$ or $\beta \in \{\alpha\}$. If $\beta \in \alpha$, then γ is in α because α is an ordinal and therefore transitive. If $\beta \in \{\alpha\}$, then $\beta = \alpha$, and so, $\gamma \in \alpha$ because $\gamma \in \beta$. This shows that $\alpha + 1$ is transitive.

           We now show that $\alpha + 1$ is antireflexive. Let $\beta \in \alpha + 1$. Then $\beta \in \alpha$ or $\beta \in \{\alpha\}$. If $\beta \in \alpha$, then $\beta \notin \beta$ because α is antireflexive. If $\beta \in \{\alpha\}$, then $\beta = \alpha$. Suppose toward contradiction that $\alpha \in \alpha$. Then α is an element of α with $\alpha \in \alpha$, contradicting that α is antireflexive. So, $\alpha + 1$ is antireflexive.

           We now show that $\alpha + 1$ is antisymmetric. Let $\beta, \gamma \in \alpha + 1$ with $\beta \in \gamma$ and $\gamma \in \beta$. Since α is antireflexive, we cannot have both β and γ in α. Without loss of generality, assume that $\beta \notin \alpha$. Then $\beta \in \{\alpha\}$, and so, $\beta = \alpha$. So, $\alpha \in \gamma$ and $\gamma \in \alpha$. Since α is transitive, $\alpha \in \alpha$, contradicting that α is antireflexive. So, $\alpha + 1$ is antisymmetric.

We now show that $\alpha + 1$ is transitive. Let $\beta, \gamma, \delta \in \alpha + 1$ with $\beta \in \gamma$ and $\gamma \in \delta$. If $\delta = \alpha$, then since α is a transitive set, $\beta \in \alpha$. So, $\beta \in \delta$. If $\delta \in \alpha$, then since α is a transitive set, $\gamma \in \alpha$, and again, since α is a transitive set, $\beta \in \alpha$. Since $\in$ is transitive on α, $\beta \in \delta$. So, $\alpha + 1$ is transitive.

We now show that $(\alpha + 1, \in)$ satisfies trichotomy. Let $\beta, \gamma \in \alpha + 1$ and assume that $\beta \notin \gamma$ and $\gamma \notin \beta$. If $\gamma = \alpha$, then since $\beta \notin \alpha$, $\beta = \alpha = \gamma$. Similarly, if $\beta = \alpha$, then since $\gamma \notin \alpha$, $\gamma = \alpha = \beta$. If $\beta \neq \alpha$ and $\gamma \neq \alpha$, then $\beta, \gamma \in \alpha$. Since $(\alpha, \in)$ satisfies trichotomy, $\beta = \gamma$. So, $(\alpha + 1, \in)$ satisfies trichotomy.

Finally, let $B \subseteq \alpha + 1$ be nonempty. If $B \setminus \{\alpha\} \neq \emptyset$, $B \setminus \{\alpha\}$ is a nonempty subset of α, and therefore, has a least element β. Since $\beta \in \alpha$, β is the least element of B as well. If $B \setminus \{\alpha\} = \emptyset$, then $B = \{\alpha\}$, and the least element of B is α. It follows that $\alpha + 1$ is well-ordered by $\in$.

Therefore, $\alpha + 1$ is an ordinal. $\qquad\square$

(ii) Let α be an ordinal and let $x \in \alpha$. Since α is transitive, $x \subseteq \alpha$. Since any subset of a well-ordered set is well-ordered, x is well-ordered by $\in$. Suppose that $y \in x$ and $z \in y$. Since $x \subseteq \alpha$, $y \in \alpha$. Since α is transitive, $z \in \alpha$. Since α is linearly ordered, $x, y, z \in \alpha$, $z \in y$, and $y \in x$, we have $z \in x$. Therefore, x is transitive. Since x is transitive and well-ordered by $\in$, x is an ordinal.

Now, let $z \in x$. Since $x \subseteq \alpha$, $z \in \alpha$. Therefore, $z \in \text{pred}(\alpha, x)$. So, $x \subseteq \text{pred}(\alpha, x)$. Let $z \in \text{pred}(\alpha, x)$. Then $z \in \alpha$ and $z \in x$. In particular, $z \in x$. So, $\text{pred}(\alpha, x) \subseteq x$. Since we have $x \subseteq \text{pred}(\alpha, x)$ and $\text{pred}(\alpha, x) \subseteq x$, it follows that $x = \text{pred}(\alpha, x)$. $\qquad\square$

6. Let $\boldsymbol{P} = \{P_0, P_1, \dots\}$ be a partition of $\mathbb{N}$ into infinitely many infinite sets (see part 1 of Problem 5 from Problem Set 7). Define $\lhd$ on $\mathbb{N}$ by

$$\lhd = \big\{(m, n) \big| (\exists k \in \mathbb{N}(m, n \in P_k \wedge m < n) \vee \exists j, k \in \mathbb{N}(j < k \wedge m \in P_j \wedge n \in P_k)\big\}.$$

Prove that $(\mathbb{N}, \lhd)$ is a well-ordered set isomorphic to the ordinal $\omega \cdot \omega$.

Proof: Checking that $(\mathbb{N}, \lhd)$ is a well-ordered set is straightforward.

Define $f \colon \mathbb{N} \to \omega \cdot \omega$ by $f(n) = \omega \cdot k + m$, where $n \in P_k$ and n has exactly m predecessors in P_k under the ordering $\lhd$. Note that for each $n \in \mathbb{N}$, k and m are uniquely determined because $\boldsymbol{P}$ is a partition of $\mathbb{N}$. Also, if $k, m \in \mathbb{N}$, then $\omega \cdot k + m \in \omega \cdot (k + 1) \in \bigcup\{\omega \cdot j \mid j \in \omega\} = \omega \cdot \omega$. So, f is in fact a function from $\mathbb{N}$ into $\omega \cdot \omega$. To see that f is injective, suppose that $f(n) = \omega \cdot k + m$, $f(t) = \omega \cdot r + s$, and $f(n) = f(t)$. So, $\omega \cdot k + m = \omega \cdot r + s$. If $k < r$, then $\omega \cdot k + m \in \omega \cdot r \in \omega \cdot r + s$, and therefore, $\omega \cdot k + m \in \omega \cdot r + s$, which is impossible. Similarly, we cannot have $r < k$. So, $r = k$. Thus, we have $\omega \cdot k + m = \omega \cdot k + s$. So, $m = s$. It follows that $n = t$. Since $n, t \in \mathbb{N}$ were arbitrary, f is injective. To see that f is surjective, let $\omega \cdot k + m \in \omega \cdot \omega$. Then $f(n) = \omega \cdot k + m$, where $n \in P_k$ and n has exactly m predecessors in P_k under the ordering $\lhd$.

Now, suppose that $n \lhd r$. If there is $k \in \mathbb{N}$ with $n, t \in P_k$ and $n < t$, then $f(n) = \omega \cdot k + m$ and $f(t) = \omega \cdot k + s$ with $m, s \in \mathbb{N}$ and $m < s$. So, $f(n) < f(t)$. If there are $j, k \in \mathbb{N}$ with $j < k$, $n \in P_j$ and $t \in P_j$, then $f(n) = \omega \cdot j + m$ (for some $m \in \mathbb{N}$) $< \omega \cdot k + t$ (for some $t \in \mathbb{N}$) $= f(t)$. Conversely, if $f(n) < f(t)$ with $f(n) = \omega \cdot k + m$ and $f(t) = \omega \cdot r + s$, then $n \in P_k$ and $t \in P_r$. If $k < r$, then $n \lhd t$ by the definition of $\lhd$. If $k = t$, then $n, t \in P_k$ and $n < t$. So, $n \lhd t$. Therefore, f is an isomorphism. $\square$

LEVEL 4

7. Let α and β be ordinals. Prove each of the following:

    (i) If α is isomorphic to β, then $\alpha = \beta$.

    (ii) Exactly one of the following holds: $\alpha = \beta$, $\alpha \in \beta$, or $\beta \in \alpha$.

Proofs:

(i) Suppose that α and β are isomorphic ordinals and let $f : \alpha \cong \beta$. We will show that $f(\gamma) = \gamma$ for each $\gamma \in \alpha$. Suppose toward contradiction that $S = \{\gamma \in \alpha \mid f(\gamma) \neq \gamma\} \neq \emptyset$. By the Ordinal Well Ordering Principle, S has a least element, say δ. Suppose that $f(\delta) = \eta$. By part (ii) of Problem 5, $\eta = \mathrm{pred}(\beta, \eta)$. Also, $\mathrm{pred}(\beta, \eta) = \{f(\tau) \mid \tau \in \delta\} = \{\tau \mid \tau \in \delta\} = \delta$. So, $f(\delta) = \eta = \delta$, contradicting our assumption that $\delta \in S$. So, $S = \emptyset$ and $f(\gamma) = \gamma$ for each $\gamma \in \alpha$. So, $\gamma \in \alpha$ if and only if $\gamma \in \beta$. Therefore, $\alpha = \beta$. $\square$

(ii) Let α and β be ordinals. If $\alpha \in \beta$ and $\beta \in \alpha$, then by the transitivity of α, $\alpha \in \alpha$. But then α is an element of α with $\alpha \in \alpha$, contradicting that α is antireflexive. So, $\alpha \in \beta$ and $\beta \in \alpha$ cannot both hold simultaneously. Also, if $\alpha \in \beta$ and $\alpha = \beta$, then $\alpha \in \alpha$, which once again is impossible. Similarly, we cannot have both $\alpha = \beta$ and $\beta \in \alpha$. So, at most one of $\alpha \in \beta$, $\alpha = \beta$, or $\beta \in \alpha$ holds.

Now, since α and β are well-ordered, by Theorem 12.7, $\alpha \cong \beta$, there is $\gamma \in \beta$ such that $\alpha \cong \mathrm{pred}(\beta, \gamma)$, or there is $\gamma \in \alpha$ such that $\beta \cong \mathrm{pred}(\alpha, \gamma)$. If $\alpha \cong \beta$, then by (i), $\alpha = \beta$. If $\alpha \cong \mathrm{pred}(\beta, \gamma)$, then by part (ii) of Problem 5, $\alpha \cong \gamma$. So, once again by (i), $\alpha = \gamma$. Thus, $\alpha \in \beta$. If $\beta \cong \mathrm{pred}(\alpha, \gamma)$, then again by part (ii) of Problem 5, $\beta \cong \gamma$. So, once again by (i), $\beta = \gamma$. Thus, $\beta \in \alpha$. $\square$

8. Prove that a transitive set of ordinals in an ordinal.

Proof: Let A be a transitive set of ordinals. We need to show that A is well-ordered by $\in$.

Let $\alpha \in A$. Since α is an ordinal, $\alpha \notin \alpha$, for otherwise, α is an element of itself that violates the antireflexivity of α. So $\in$ is antireflexive on A.

Let $\alpha, \beta \in A$. If $\alpha \in \beta$ and $\beta \in \alpha$, then by the transitivity of α, $\alpha \in \alpha$, which once again is impossible. So, $\alpha \in \beta$ and $\beta \in \alpha$ cannot hold, and so, $\in$ is antisymmetric on A.

Let $\alpha, \beta, \gamma \in A$ with $\alpha \in \beta$ and $\beta \in \gamma$. Then by the transitivity of γ, $\alpha \in \gamma$. So, $\in$ is transitive on A.

Let $\alpha, \beta \in A$. Since α and β are ordinals, by part (ii) of Problem 7, exactly one of the following holds: $\alpha = \beta$, $\alpha \in \beta$, or $\beta \in \alpha$. So, $(A, \in)$ satisfies trichotomy.

Let B be a nonempty subset of A and let $\alpha \in B$ be arbitrary. If α is not the $\in$-least element of B, let β be the $\in$-least element of $B \cap \alpha$. If $\gamma \in B$ with $\gamma \in \beta$, then by the transitivity of α, $\gamma \in \alpha$. Therefore, $\gamma \in B \cap \alpha$, contradicting that β is the $\in$-least element of $B \cap \alpha$. So, β is the $\in$-least element of B. It follows that A is well-ordered by $\in$.

Since A is transitive and well-ordered by $\in$, A is an ordinal. $\qquad\square$

LEVEL 5

9. Let X be a set of ordinals. Prove the following:

    (i) $\bigcup X$ is the least ordinal greater than or equal to all elements of X.

    (ii)   If $X \neq \emptyset$, then $\bigcap X$ is the least ordinal in X.

Proofs:

(i) If $\alpha \in \bigcup X$, then there is $\beta \in X$ with $\alpha \in \beta$. Since β is an ordinal, β is transitive. Therefore, $\alpha \subseteq \beta$. Since $\beta \subseteq \bigcup X$, $\alpha \subseteq \bigcup X$. Since $\alpha \in \bigcup X$ was arbitrary, $\bigcup X$ is transitive. It is also straightforward to check that $\bigcup X$ is well-ordered by $\in$. Therefore, $\bigcup X$ is an ordinal.

Suppose $\alpha \in X$. Then $\alpha \subseteq \bigcup X$. Since α and $\bigcup X$ are both ordinals, we must have $\alpha \in \bigcup X$, $\alpha = \bigcup X$, or $\bigcup X \in \alpha$. Now, if $\bigcup X \in \alpha$, then since $\alpha \subseteq \bigcup X$, $\bigcup X \in \bigcup X$, which is impossible. So, $\alpha \in \bigcup X$ or $\alpha = \bigcup X$. That is $\alpha \leq \bigcup X$. Since $\alpha \in X$ was arbitrary, we see that $\bigcup X$ is greater than or equal to all elements of X.

Now, suppose that there is an ordinal β such that $\alpha \in \beta$ for all $\alpha \in X$. Let $\gamma \in \bigcup X$. Then there is $\alpha \in X$ with $\gamma \in \alpha$. Since $\alpha \in X$, we have $\alpha \in \beta$. By the transitivity of β, $\gamma \in \beta$. Since $\gamma \in \bigcup X$ was arbitrary, $\bigcup X \subseteq \beta$. We cannot have $\beta \in \bigcup X$, because then we would have $\beta \in \beta$. Therefore, $\bigcup X \leq \beta$. It follows that $\bigcup X$ is the **least** ordinal greater than or equal to all elements of X. $\qquad\square$

(ii) Let $\alpha \in \bigcap X$ and $\beta \in \alpha$. If $\gamma \in X$, then we have $\beta \in \alpha \in \gamma$. So, $\beta \in \gamma$ for all $\gamma \in X$. Therefore, $\beta \in \bigcap X$. Since $\beta \in \alpha$ was arbitrary, $\alpha \subseteq \bigcap X$. Since $\alpha \in \bigcap X$ was arbitrary, $\bigcap X$ is transitive. It is also straightforward to check that $\bigcap X$ is well-ordered by $\in$. Therefore, $\bigcap X$ is an ordinal.

Let α be the least ordinal in X. Let $\beta \in \alpha$ and $\gamma \in X$. Since α is the least ordinal in X, $\gamma = \alpha$ or $\alpha \in \gamma$. In either case, $\beta \in \gamma$. So, $\beta \in \gamma$ for every $\gamma \in X$. Therefore, $\beta \in \bigcap X$. Since $\beta \in \alpha$ was arbitrary, $\alpha \subseteq \bigcap X$. Now, let $\beta \in \bigcap X$. Since $\alpha \in X$, $\beta \in \alpha$. Since $\beta \in \bigcap X$ was arbitrary, $\bigcap X \subseteq \alpha$. Since $\alpha \subseteq \bigcap X$ and $\bigcap X \subseteq \alpha$, we have $\bigcap X = \alpha$. Therefore, $\bigcap X$ is the least ordinal in X. $\qquad\square$

10. Let $(W, <)$ be a well-ordered set. Prove that there is a unique ordinal α such that $W \cong \alpha$.

Proof: Let $(W, <)$ be a well-ordered set and let $B = \{a \in W \mid \exists \beta (\beta \text{ is an ordinal} \wedge \mathrm{pred}(W, a) \cong \beta)\}$. Let f be the function with domain B, where $f(a)$ is the unique ordinal β_a such that $\mathrm{pred}(W, a) \cong \beta_a$. The ordinal β_a is unique by part (i) of Problem 7.

Let C be the range of f. Note that C is a set of ordinals. We first show that C is transitive.

To see this, let $\beta_a \in C$ and $\gamma \in \beta_a$. Let $g\colon \mathrm{pred}(W, a) \cong \beta_a$. Since $\gamma \in \beta_a$, there is $b \in \mathrm{pred}(W, a)$ such that $g(b) = \gamma$. Let h be the restriction of g to $\mathrm{pred}(W, b)$. Let's check that $h\colon \mathrm{pred}(W, b) \cong \gamma$.

First note that if $c \in \mathrm{pred}(W, b)$, then $c < b$, and so, $h(c) = g(c) \in g(b) = \gamma$. So, h does in fact map $\mathrm{pred}(W, b)$ to γ.

To see that h is injective, let $c, d \in \mathrm{pred}(W, b)$ with $c < d$. Then $h(c) = g(c) \in g(d) = h(d)$, and in particular, $h(c) \neq h(d)$.

To see that h is surjective, let $\delta \in \gamma$. Since β_a is an ordinal, by Problem 2, $\delta \in \beta_a$. Since g is surjective, there is $c \in \mathrm{pred}(W, a)$ with $g(c) = \delta$. Since $g(c) = \delta \in \gamma = g(b)$ and g is a homomorphism, $c < b$. Therefore, $c \in \mathrm{pred}(W, b)$, and so, $h(c) = g(c)$.

To see that h is a homomorphism, let $c, d \in \mathrm{pred}(W, b)$. Then $c < d$ if and only if $g(c) \in g(d)$ if and only if $h(c) \in h(d)$.

Also, by part (ii) of Problem 5, γ is an ordinal. It follows that $\gamma \in C$ and therefore, C is transitive.

Since C is a transitive set of ordinals, by Problem 8, C is an ordinal, say $C = \alpha$.

We now show that B is an initial segment of W. Let $b \in B$ and $c < b$. Let $g\colon \mathrm{pred}(W, b) \cong \beta_b$. Since $c < b$, $c \in \mathrm{pred}(W, b)$. Let $g(c) = \gamma \in \beta_b$. Then by a reason similar to what was done above, $\mathrm{pred}(W, c) \cong \gamma$.

Next, we show that $f\colon B \to \alpha$ is an isomorphism.

To see that f is injective, let $c, d \in B$ with $c < d$ and let $g\colon \mathrm{pred}(W, d) \cong \beta_d$. By Theorem 12.6, g is f restricted to $\mathrm{pred}(W, d)$. Since $c < d$, $f(c) = g(c) \in \beta_d = f(d)$. In particular, $f(c) \neq f(d)$.

f is surjective by the definition of α.

To see that f is a homomorphism, let $c, d \in B$. The argument for injectivity showed that $c < d$ implies $f(c) \in f(d)$. If $f(c) \in f(d)$, let $g\colon \mathrm{pred}(W, d) \cong \beta_d = f(d)$. By Theorem 12.6, g is f restricted to $\mathrm{pred}(W, d)$. So, $g(c) \in g(d)$. Since g is an isomorphism, $c < d$.

Finally, we show that $B = W$. Assume toward contradiction that B is a proper initial segment of W. Then $W \setminus B \neq \emptyset$. Let $b \in W \setminus B$ with $B = \mathrm{pred}(W, b)$. Then $\mathrm{pred}(W, b) \cong \alpha$. So, $b \in B$, a contradiction. $\qquad \square$

Problem Set 13

LEVEL 1

1. Let κ and λ be infinite cardinals. Prove each of the following:

   (i) $\kappa + \lambda = \max\{\kappa, \lambda\}$.

   (ii) $\kappa \cdot \lambda = \max\{\kappa, \lambda\}$.

   (iii) For each natural number $n \geq 1$, $\kappa^n = \kappa$.

Proofs:

(i) Without loss of generality, let $\max\{\kappa, \lambda\} = \kappa$. Then $\max\{\kappa, \lambda\} = \kappa \leq \kappa + \lambda$. Also, since $(\kappa \times \{0\}) \cup (\lambda \times \{1\}) \subseteq \kappa \times \lambda$, we have

$\kappa + \lambda = |(\kappa \times \{0\}) \cup (\lambda \times \{1\})| \leq |\kappa \times \lambda| = \kappa \cdot \lambda \leq \kappa \cdot \kappa = \kappa$ (by Theorem 13.2) $= \max\{\kappa, \lambda\}$.

Since $\kappa + \lambda \leq \max\{\kappa, \lambda\}$ and $\max\{\kappa, \lambda\} \leq \kappa + \lambda$, we have $\kappa + \lambda = \max\{\kappa, \lambda\}$. □

(ii) Without loss of generality, let $\max\{\kappa, \lambda\} = \kappa$. Then $\max\{\kappa, \lambda\} = \kappa \leq |\kappa \times \lambda| = \kappa \cdot \lambda$ and

$$\kappa \cdot \lambda = |\kappa \times \lambda| \leq |\kappa \times \kappa| = \kappa \cdot \kappa = \kappa \text{ (by Theorem 13.2)} = \max\{\kappa, \lambda\}.$$

Since $\kappa \cdot \lambda \leq \max\{\kappa, \lambda\}$ and $\max\{\kappa, \lambda\} \leq \kappa \cdot \lambda$, we have $\kappa \cdot \lambda = \max\{\kappa, \lambda\}$. □

(iii) We prove by induction that $\kappa^n = \kappa$ for all $n \geq 1$.

Base case ($n = 1$): $\kappa^1 = \kappa$.

Inductive step: Suppose that $\kappa^j = \kappa$. Then $\kappa^{j+1} = \kappa^j \cdot \kappa^1 = \kappa \cdot \kappa = \kappa$.

By the Principle of Mathematical Induction, $\kappa^n = \kappa$ for all $n \geq 1$. □

2. Let κ, λ, and μ be infinite cardinals. Prove that $\kappa^\lambda \kappa^\mu = \kappa^{\lambda + \mu}$.

Proof: Without loss of generality, assume that $\lambda \geq \mu$. We first show that $\kappa^\lambda \geq \kappa^\mu$. To see this, we define $F \colon \kappa^\mu \to \kappa^\lambda$ by $F(f) = g$, where $g(\alpha) = f(\alpha)$ for all $\alpha \in \mu$ and $g(\alpha) = 0$ for all $\alpha \in \lambda \setminus \mu$. It is easily checked that F is injective.

Since κ and λ are infinite, by the same argument above, $\kappa^\lambda \geq \kappa^\omega$. Also, $\kappa^\omega \geq 2^\omega > \omega$. By Problem 1, $\kappa^\lambda \kappa^\mu = \max\{\kappa^\lambda, \kappa^\mu\} = \kappa^\lambda$.

By our assumption that $\lambda \geq \mu$ and Problem 1, $\lambda + \mu = \max\{\lambda, \mu\} = \lambda$. So, $\kappa^{\lambda + \mu} = \kappa^\lambda$.

Therefore, $\kappa^\lambda \kappa^\mu = \kappa^\lambda = \kappa^{\lambda + \mu}$. □

LEVEL 2

3. Let κ be an infinite cardinal and let $X = \bigcup\{\kappa^n \mid n \in \omega\}$. Prove that $|X| = \kappa$.

Proof: Since $\kappa \subseteq X$, $\kappa \leq |X|$. By Problem 1 (part (iii)), for each $n \in \omega$, there is an injection $f_n: \kappa^n \to \kappa$. We define $g: X \to \kappa \times \omega$ by $g((\alpha_1, \alpha_2, ..., \alpha_n)) = (f_n((\alpha_1, \alpha_2, ..., \alpha_n)), n)$. It is easy to see that g is an injection. So, $|X| \leq \kappa \cdot \omega = \kappa$. By the Cantor-Schroeder-Bernstein Theorem, $|X| = \kappa$. □

4. Let κ be an infinite cardinal and for each ordinal $\alpha < \kappa$ let X_α be a set such that $|X_\alpha| \leq \kappa$. Prove that $|\bigcup\{X_\alpha \mid \alpha < \kappa\}| \leq \kappa$.

Proof: For each $\alpha < \kappa$, let $f_\alpha: X_\alpha \to \kappa$ be an injection. Define $g: \bigcup\{X_\alpha \mid \alpha < \kappa\} \to \kappa \times \kappa$ by $g(x) = (f_\alpha(x), \alpha)$, where α is the least ordinal such that $x \in X_\alpha$.

To see that g is injective, let $x, y \in \bigcup\{X_\alpha \mid \alpha < \kappa\}$ with $g(x) = g(y)$. Then $(f_\alpha(x), \alpha) = (f_\beta(y), \beta)$, where α is the least ordinal such that $x \in X_\alpha$ and β is the least ordinal such that $y \in X_\beta$. Since $(f_\alpha(x), \alpha) = (f_\beta(y), \beta)$, we must have $\alpha = \beta$. Therefore, $f_\alpha(x) = f_\beta(y) = f_\alpha(y)$. Since f_α is injective, $x = y$. Since $x, y \in \bigcup\{X_\alpha \mid \alpha < \kappa\}$ were arbitrary, g is injective.

It follows that $|\bigcup\{X_\alpha \mid \alpha < \kappa\}| \leq |\kappa \times \kappa| = \kappa$ (by Theorem 13.2). □

LEVEL 3

5. Let X be a set of cardinals. Prove that $\bigcup X$ is a cardinal.

Proof: By part (i) of Problem 9 from Problem Set 12, $\bigcup X$ is an ordinal. Suppose toward contradiction that $|\bigcup X| \in \bigcup X$. Then there is $\kappa \in X$ with $|\bigcup X| \in \kappa$. Again, by the same problem just mentioned, $\kappa \in \bigcup X$. Therefore, $\kappa = |\kappa| \leq |\bigcup X|$. So, we have $\kappa \in \kappa$, which is impossible. Therefore, $|\bigcup X| = \bigcup X$. So, $\bigcup X$ is a cardinal. □

6. Let κ be an infinite cardinal. Define the relation $\lhd$ on $\kappa \times \kappa$ by $(\alpha, \beta) \lhd (\gamma, \delta)$ if and only if

   (i) $\max\{\alpha, \beta\} \in \max\{\gamma, \delta\}$; or

   (ii) $\max\{\alpha, \beta\} = \max\{\gamma, \delta\}$ and $\alpha \in \gamma$; or

   (iii) $\max\{\alpha, \beta\} = \max\{\gamma, \delta\}$ and $\alpha = \gamma$ and $\beta \in \delta$.

   Prove that $(\kappa \times \kappa, \lhd)$ is a well-ordered set.

Proof: To see that $\lhd$ is antireflexive on $\kappa \times \kappa$, let $(\alpha, \beta) \in \kappa \times \kappa$. First assume that $\alpha \leq \beta$ (in the sense that $\alpha \in \beta$ or $\alpha = \beta$). Then $\max\{\alpha, \beta\} = \beta$. Since β is an ordinal, $\beta \notin \beta$, and so, (i) and (iii) fail. Since α is an ordinal, $\alpha \notin \alpha$. So, (ii) fails. The case where $\beta \in \alpha$ is similar. So, $(\alpha, \beta) \not\lhd (\alpha, \beta)$. Therefore, $\lhd$ is antireflexive.

To see that $\lhd$ is antisymmetric on $\kappa \times \kappa$, let $(\alpha, \beta), (\gamma, \delta) \in \kappa \times \kappa$ and assume that $(\alpha, \beta) \lhd (\gamma, \delta)$ and $(\gamma, \delta) \lhd (\alpha, \beta)$. First assume that $\alpha \leq \beta$ and $\gamma \leq \delta$, so that $\max\{\alpha, \beta\} = \beta$ and $\max\{\gamma, \delta\} = \delta$. If $\beta \in \delta$, then we cannot have $\delta \in \beta$ or $\delta = \beta$. So, $\beta = \delta$ and $\alpha \in \gamma$. But then we cannot have $\gamma \in \alpha$ or $\gamma = \alpha$. Therefore, $\alpha \leq \beta$ and $\gamma \leq \delta$ is impossible. Similar arguments show that the other three possibilities are impossible as well. So, we cannot have both $(\alpha, \beta) \lhd (\gamma, \delta)$ and $(\gamma, \delta) \lhd (\alpha, \beta)$. Therefore, $\lhd$ is vacuously antisymmetric on $\kappa \times \kappa$.

80

To see that $\lhd$ is transitive on $\kappa \times \kappa$, let $(\alpha, \beta), (\gamma, \delta), (\eta, \xi) \in \kappa \times \kappa$ and assume that $(\alpha, \beta) \lhd (\gamma, \delta)$ and $(\gamma, \delta) \lhd (\eta, \xi)$. First assume that $\alpha \leq \beta$, $\gamma \leq \delta$, and $\eta \leq \xi$ so that $\max\{\alpha, \beta\} = \beta$, $\max\{\gamma, \delta\} = \delta$, and $\max\{\eta, \xi\} = \xi$. If $\beta \in \delta$ and $\delta \in \xi$, then by the transitivity of ξ, we have $\beta \in \xi$. If $\beta = \delta$ and $\delta \in \xi$, then by a simple substitution, $\beta \in \xi$. If $\beta \in \delta$ and $\delta = \xi$, then $\beta \in \xi$, again by a substitution. If $\beta = \delta$, $\delta = \xi$, $\alpha \in \gamma$, and $\gamma \in \eta$, then by the transitivity of η, $\alpha \in \eta$. This takes care of all possibilities when $\alpha \leq \beta$, $\gamma \leq \delta$, and $\eta \leq \xi$. The other seven cases are similar, and all eight cases together prove that $\lhd$ is transitive on $\kappa \times \kappa$.

To see that $(\kappa \times \kappa, \lhd)$ satisfies trichotomy, let $(\alpha, \beta), (\gamma, \delta) \in \kappa \times \kappa$ and assume that $(\alpha, \beta) \ntriangleleft (\gamma, \delta)$. First assume that $\alpha \leq \beta$ and $\gamma \leq \delta$. Since $(\alpha, \beta) \ntriangleleft (\gamma, \delta)$, $\beta \notin \delta$. So, either $\delta \in \beta$ or $\beta = \delta$. If $\delta \in \beta$, then $(\gamma, \delta) \lhd (\alpha, \beta)$. If $\beta = \delta$, then $\alpha \notin \gamma$. So, either $\gamma \in \alpha$ or $\alpha = \gamma$. If $\gamma \in \alpha$, then $(\gamma, \delta) \lhd (\alpha, \beta)$. If $\alpha = \gamma$, then $(\alpha, \beta) = (\gamma, \delta)$. The other three cases are similar, and all four cases together prove that $(\kappa \times \kappa, \lhd)$ satisfies trichotomy.

Finally, let S be a nonempty subset of $\kappa \times \kappa$. Let $A = \{\max\{\gamma, \delta\} \mid (\gamma, \delta) \in S\}$. Since $S \neq \emptyset$, $A \neq \emptyset$. Let η be the $\in$-least element of A. Let $B = \{\delta \mid (\delta, \eta) \in S\}$ and let $C = \{\delta \mid (\eta, \delta) \in S\}$. Let γ be the least element of B if it exists and let ϵ be the least element of C if it exists. Note that at least one of γ or ϵ must exist. Finally, let $(\alpha, \beta) = \min\{(\gamma, \eta), (\eta, \epsilon)\}$ under the ordering $\lhd$. Then (α, β) is the $\lhd$-least element of S. Therefore, $(\kappa \times \kappa, \lhd)$ is a well-ordered set. $\square$

LEVEL 4

7. Prove that every infinite successor cardinal is regular.

Proof: Let κ be an infinite successor cardinal. Then $\kappa = \alpha^+$ for some ordinal α. Suppose toward contradiction that $cf(\kappa) < \kappa$. Then there is an ordinal $\beta < \kappa$ and a cofinal map $f : \beta \to \kappa$. It follows that $\kappa = \bigcup\{f(\gamma) \mid \gamma \in \beta\}$. Now, for each $\gamma \in \beta$, $|f(\gamma)| < \kappa$. So, $|f(\gamma)| \leq |\alpha|$. Also, since $\beta < \kappa$, we have $|\beta| < \kappa$. So, $|\beta| \leq |\alpha|$. By Problem 4, $\kappa = |\bigcup\{f(\gamma) \mid \gamma \in \beta\}| \leq |\alpha| \leq \alpha < \kappa$, a contradiction. $\square$

8. Prove that for any ordinal α, there exists a strictly increasing cofinal function $f : cf(\alpha) \to \alpha$.

Proof: If $\alpha = \beta + 1$, then $cf(\alpha) = 1$ and the function $f : 1 \to \alpha$ defined by $f(0) = \beta$ is a strictly increasing cofinal function.

Let α be a limit ordinal and let $g : cf(\alpha) \to \alpha$ be any cofinal map. We define $f : cf(\alpha) \to \alpha$. Assuming that $f(\eta)$ has been defined for each ordinal $\eta < \xi$, let $f(\xi) = \max\{g(\xi), \bigcup\{f(\eta) + 1 \mid \eta < \xi\}\}$.

First observe that since $\xi < cf(\alpha)$, we must have $\bigcup\{f(\eta) + 1 \mid \eta < \xi\} < \alpha$ (otherwise, the function $h : \xi \to \alpha$ defined by $h(\eta) = f(\eta) + 1$ would be a cofinal function). Therefore, for each $\xi < cf(\alpha)$, $f(\xi) < \alpha$. So, $f : cf(\alpha) \to \alpha$.

Since $f(\xi) \geq g(\xi)$ for each $\xi < cf(\alpha)$, f is cofinal.

Finally, if $\xi < \tau$, $f(\xi) < f(\xi) + 1 \leq \bigcup\{f(\eta) + 1 \mid \eta < \tau\} \leq f(\tau)$. So, f is strictly increasing. $\square$

81

9. Let α be a limit ordinal and let $f: \alpha \to \beta$ be a strictly increasing cofinal function. Prove that $cf(\alpha) = cf(\beta)$.

Proof: Let α be a limit ordinal and let $f: \alpha \to \beta$ be a strictly increasing cofinal function. Also, let $g: cf(\alpha) \to \alpha$ be a cofinal function. Then $f \circ g: cf(\alpha) \to \beta$ is cofinal. To see this, let $\delta \in \beta$. Since f is cofinal, there is $\gamma \in \alpha$ with $\delta \leq f(\gamma)$. Since g is cofinal, there is $\eta \in cf(\alpha)$ with $\gamma \leq g(\eta)$. Since f is increasing, $f(\gamma) \leq f(g(\eta))$. So, we have $\delta \leq f(\gamma) \leq f(g(\eta)) = (f \circ g)(\eta)$.

Since we have found a cofinal map from $cf(\alpha)$ to β, $cf(\beta) \leq cf(\alpha)$.

Now, let $h: cf(\beta) \to \beta$ be cofinal. Define $k: cf(\beta) \to \alpha$ by

$$k(\xi) = \text{"the least } \eta < \alpha \text{ such that } h(\xi) < f(\eta)\text{."}$$

Then k is cofinal. To see this, let $\gamma \in \alpha$. Then $f(\gamma) \in \beta$. Since h is cofinal, there is $\xi \in cf(\beta)$ with $f(\gamma) \leq h(\xi)$. If $k(\xi) = \eta$, then $h(\xi) < f(\eta)$. So, $f(\gamma) < f(\eta)$. Since f is strictly increasing, $\gamma < \eta = k(\xi)$.

Since we have found a cofinal map from $cf(\beta)$ to α, $cf(\alpha) \leq cf(\beta)$.

Since $cf(\beta) \leq cf(\alpha)$ and $cf(\alpha) \leq cf(\beta)$, we have $cf(\alpha) = cf(\beta)$. $\square$

10. Prove that for any ordinal α, $cf(cf(\alpha)) = cf(\alpha)$.

Proof: If $\alpha = \beta + 1$, then $cf(\alpha) = 1$ and so, $cf(cf(\alpha)) = cf(1) = 1$. So, the result holds.

Let α be a limit ordinal. Then $cf(\alpha)$ is also a limit ordinal. By Problem 8 there is a strictly increasing cofinal function $f: cf(\alpha) \to \alpha$. By Problem 9, $cf(cf(\alpha)) = cf(\alpha)$. $\square$

Problem Set 14

LEVEL 1

1. Let $\mathcal{A}$ be an infinite almost disjoint family with $|\mathcal{A}| < 2^\omega$ and let $\mathbb{P}_\mathcal{A}$ be the corresponding mad poset. Prove that for each $A \in \mathcal{A}$, $\mathcal{D}_A = \{(s, \mathcal{A}_0) \in \mathbb{P}_\mathcal{A} \mid A \in \mathcal{A}_0\}$ is dense.

Proof: Let $(s, \mathcal{A}_0) \in \mathbb{P}_\mathcal{A}$. Then $(s, \mathcal{A}_0 \cup \{A\}) \in \mathcal{D}_A$ because $A \in \mathcal{A}_0 \cup \{A\}$. Also, we have $(s, \mathcal{A}_0 \cup \{A\}) \leq (s, \mathcal{A}_0)$ because $s \subseteq s$, $\mathcal{A}_0 \subseteq \mathcal{A}_0 \cup \{A\}$, and $s \cap B = s \cap B$ for all $B \in \mathcal{A}_0$. □

2. Use Zorn's Lemma to prove that any almost disjoint family can be extended to a mad family.

Proof: Let $\mathcal{A}$ be an almost disjoint family and let

$$P = \{\mathcal{B} \subseteq \mathcal{P}(\omega) \mid \mathcal{A} \subseteq \mathcal{B} \text{ and } \mathcal{B} \text{ is an almost disjoint family}\}.$$

Then P is partially ordered by inclusion. If $\mathcal{C}$ is a chain in P, then it is easy to see that $\bigcup \mathcal{C}$ is an upper bound of $\mathcal{C}$. By Zorn's Lemma, P has a maximal element, which is a mad family extending $\mathcal{A}$. □

LEVEL 2

3. Let $\mathcal{A}$ be an infinite almost disjoint family with $|\mathcal{A}| < 2^\omega$ and let $\mathbb{P}_\mathcal{A}$ be the corresponding mad poset. Prove that $\mathbb{P}_\mathcal{A}$ has the c.c.c.

Proof: Assume towards contradiction that $\{p_i = (s_i, \mathcal{A}_i) \mid i \in I\}$ is an antichain, where I is an uncountable set. Since $\{s \mid s \text{ is a finite subset of } \omega\}$ is a countable set, there must exist s and an uncountable set $J \subseteq I$ such that $\{p_i = (s, \mathcal{A}_i) \mid i \in I\}$ is still an uncountable antichain. Let $i, j \in J$ and let $r = (s, \mathcal{A}_i \cup \mathcal{A}_j)$. Then $r \leq p_i$ and $r \leq p_j$, and so, p_i and p_j are compatible, contradicting our assumption that $\{p_i = (s_i, \mathcal{A}_i) \mid i \in I\}$ is an antichain. So, $\mathbb{P}_\mathcal{A}$ has no uncountable antichains. □

4. Let $\mathcal{A}$ be an infinite almost disjoint family with $|\mathcal{A}| < 2^\omega$ and let $\mathbb{P}_\mathcal{A}$ be the corresponding mad poset. Prove that for each $n \in \omega$, $\mathcal{E}_n = \{(s, \mathcal{A}_0) \in \mathbb{P}_\mathcal{A} \mid \exists m \in s (m > n)\}$ is dense.

Proof: Let $p = (s, \mathcal{A}_0) \in \mathbb{P}_\mathcal{A}$, where $\mathcal{A}_0 = \{A_0, A_1, \ldots, A_k\}$. If $p \in \mathcal{E}_n$, we are done. So, assume that $p \notin \mathcal{E}_n$. We can find $m \in \omega \setminus (A_0 \cup A_1 \cup \cdots \cup A_k \cup \{0, 1, \ldots, n\})$. Then $(s \cup \{m\}, \mathcal{A}_0) \in \mathcal{E}_n$ because $m \in s \cup \{m\}$ and $m > n$. Also, $(s \cup \{m\}, \mathcal{A}_0) \leq (s, \mathcal{A}_0)$ because $s \subseteq s \cup \{m\}$, $\mathcal{A}_0 \subseteq \mathcal{A}_0$, and for all $A \in \mathcal{A}_0 (s \cap A = (s \cup \{m\}) \cap A)$. □

LEVEL 3

5. Prove that there does not exist a denumerable mad family.

Proof: Suppose toward contradiction that $\mathcal{A} \subseteq \mathcal{P}(\omega)$ is a denumerable mad family. We first show that for any $n \in \omega$ and distinct $A_0, A_1, \ldots, A_n \in \mathcal{A}$, $\omega \setminus \{A_0 \cup A_1 \cdots \cup A_n\}$ is infinite. To see this, let $A \in \mathcal{A} \setminus \{A_0, A_1, \ldots, A_n\}$. Then $A \setminus [(A_0 \cap A) \cup (A_1 \cap A) \cup \cdots \cup (A_n \cap A)] \subseteq \omega \setminus \{A_0 \cup A_1 \cdots \cup A_n\}$. Now, $A \setminus [(A_0 \cap A) \cup (A_1 \cap A) \cup \cdots \cup (A_n \cap A)]$ is infinite because $A_0 \cap A, A_1 \cap A, \ldots, A_n \cap A$ are each finite and A is infinite, Therefore, $\omega \setminus \{A_0 \cup A_1 \cdots \cup A_n\}$ is infinite.

We can now define, by induction on $n \in \omega$, distinct elements $\{b_n \mid n \in \omega\}$ such that for each $n \in \omega$, we have $b_{n+1} \in \omega \setminus (A_0 \cup A_1 \cdots \cup A_n \cup \{b_0, b_1, \ldots, b_n\})$. Let $B = \{b_n \mid n \in \omega\}$. Then $\mathcal{A} \cup \{B\}$ is a mad family, contradicting the maximality of $\mathcal{A}$. $\qquad\square$

6. Prove that MA(2^ω) is false.

Proof: Consider the poset $\mathbb{P}\omega_\omega$. If $\mathcal{G} \subseteq \mathbb{P}\omega_\omega$ were a filter such that $\mathcal{G} \cap \mathcal{D}_f \neq \emptyset$ for all $f \in \mathcal{F}$ and $\mathcal{G} \cap \mathcal{E}_k \neq \emptyset$ for all $k \in \omega$, then by Theorem 14.2 there would be a function $g \in {}^\omega\omega$ such that $f <^* g$ for all $f \in {}^\omega\omega$. Since no function can dominate itself, this is impossible. Note that $|{}^\omega\omega| = |{}^\omega 2|$ (by part 5 of Example 7.1 and part (iv) of Problem 7 in Problem Set 7). Thus, MA(2^ω) is false. $\qquad\square$

LEVEL 4

7. Prove that MA(ω) is true.

Proof: Let $\mathbb{P}$ be a nonempty c.c.c. poset and $\mathcal{D}$ a family of at most ω dense subsets of $\mathbb{P}$, say $\mathcal{D} = \{D_n \mid n \in \omega\}$. We can inductively define a sequence $p_0 \geq p_1 \geq \cdots \geq p_n \geq \cdots$ such that for each $n \in \omega$, $p_n \in D_n$. We can let p_0 be any element of D_0, and having chosen p_k, we use the fact that D_{k+1} is dense to choose $p_{k+1} \in D_{k+1}$ such that $p_{k+1} \leq p_k$. Now, we let $\mathcal{G} = \{q \in \mathbb{P} \mid \exists n(p_n \leq q)\}$. It is easy to see that $\mathcal{G} \subseteq \mathbb{P}$ is a filter that intersects each $D_n \in \mathcal{D}$. So MA(ω) is true. $\qquad\square$

8. Let $\mathbb{P} = \{f \mid f : n \to \omega_1 \text{ for some } n < \omega\}$ ordered by $f \leq h$ if and only if $h \subseteq f$. Let $\mathcal{G} \subseteq \mathbb{P}$ be a filter intersecting each of the sets $E_k = \{f \mid k \in \mathrm{dom}\, f\}$ for each $k < \omega$ and $D_\alpha = \{f \mid \alpha \in \mathrm{ran}\, f\}$ for each $\alpha < \omega_1$. Assume that CH is false. Prove that $g = \bigcup \mathcal{G}$ is a surjective function from ω to ω_1 and explain why this does not prove that MA is inconsistent.

Proof: It is easy to see that each E_k is dense and each D_α is dense. Let $k \in \omega$ and let $f \in \mathcal{G} \cap E_k$. Then $f \subseteq \bigcup \mathcal{G} = g$. Since $(k, f(k)) \in f$, we have $(k, f(k)) \in g$. So, $k \in \mathrm{dom}\, g$. Since $k \in \omega$ was arbitrary, $\mathrm{dom}\, g = \omega$. Now, let $\alpha \in \omega_1$ and let $f \in \mathcal{G} \cap D_\alpha$. Again, $f \subseteq \bigcup \mathcal{G} = g$. Since $f \in D_\alpha$, $\alpha \in \mathrm{ran}\, f$, and so, there is $k \in \omega$ with $(k, \alpha) \in f$. So, $(k, \alpha) \in g$. Since $\alpha \in \omega_1$ was arbitrary, $\mathrm{ran}\, g = \omega_1$. Now, suppose that $(k, \alpha), (k, \beta) \in g$. Then there are $f, h \in \mathcal{G}$ with $(k, \alpha) \in f$ and $(k, \beta) \in h$. Since $\mathcal{G}$ is a filter, there is $b \in \mathcal{G}$ with $b \leq f, h$. Then $(k, \alpha), (k, \beta) \in b$. Since b is a function, $\alpha = \beta$. Since $(k, \alpha), (k, \beta) \in g$ were arbitrary, we see that g is a function.

Now, for each $\alpha \in \omega_1$, let $f_\alpha = \{(0, \alpha)\}$. If $\alpha \neq \beta$, then $f_\alpha \perp f_\beta$ because a common extension would contain $(0, \alpha)$ and $(0, \beta)$, and therefore, would not be a function. So, $\{f_\alpha \mid \alpha \in \omega_1\}$ is an antichain. Clearly this antichain has size ω_1, and so, it it uncountable. Therefore, $\mathbb{P}$ does not have the c.c.c. So, MA cannot be used to prove the existence of g. $\qquad\square$

LEVEL 5

9. We will say that A is **almost a subset** of B, written $A \subseteq^* B$ if $B \setminus A$ is finite. If $\mathcal{A}$ is a family of sets, then a **pseudointersection** of A is an infinite set that is almost a subset of every member of $\mathcal{A}$. A **tower** is a collection $\{T_\alpha \mid \alpha < \lambda\}$ such that (a) Each T_α is an infinite subset of ω, (b) $\alpha < \beta < \lambda \to T_\alpha \subseteq^* T_\beta$, and (c) $\{T_\alpha \mid \alpha < \lambda\}$ has no pseudointersection. Prove that a countably infinite tower is not maximal.

Proof: Let $\mathcal{T} = \{T_n \mid n \in \omega\}$ be a tower and define $T = \{t_n \mid n \in \omega\}$ inductively as follows: Let $t_0 \in T_0$ be arbitrary. Having chosen t_n, choose $t_{n+1} \in \cap\{T_k \mid k < n + 1\}$ such that $t_{n+1} > t_n$. For each $n \in \omega$, we have $\{t_k \mid k \geq n\} \subseteq T_n$. Thus, $T \subseteq^* T_n$. Therefore, $\mathcal{T}$ is not maximal. $\qquad \square$

10. Prove that if MA holds, then every maximal infinite tower has cardinality 2^ω.

Proof: Let $\mathcal{T} = \{T_\alpha \mid \alpha < \lambda\}$ be a tower of infinite cardinality $\lambda < 2^\omega$ and let $\mathbb{P}_{\mathcal{T}} = (P, \leq)$ be defined as follows:

1. P consists of pairs $(s, \mathcal{T}_0)$, where

    (i) s is a finite subset of ω.

    (ii) $\mathcal{T}_0$ is a finite subset of $\mathcal{T}$.

2. If $(s, \mathcal{T}_0), (t, \mathcal{T}_1) \in P$, then $(t, \mathcal{T}_1) \leq (s, \mathcal{T}_0)$ if and only if each of the following holds.

    (i) $s \subseteq t$.

    (ii) $\mathcal{T}_0 \subseteq \mathcal{T}_1$.

    (iii) For all $n \in t \setminus s(n \in \cap \mathcal{T}_0)$.

It is straightforward to check that, $\mathbb{P}_{\mathcal{T}}$ has the c.c.c., for each $\alpha < \lambda$, $\mathcal{D}_\alpha = \{(s, \mathcal{T}_0) \in \mathbb{P}_{\mathcal{T}} \mid T_\alpha \in \mathcal{T}_0\}$ is dense, and for each $n \in \omega$, $\mathcal{E}_n = \{(s, \mathcal{T}_0) \in \mathbb{P}_{\mathcal{T}} \mid \exists m \in s(m > n)\}$ is dense.

By MA, there is a filter $\mathcal{G} \subseteq \mathbb{P}_{\mathcal{T}}$ such that $\mathcal{G} \cap \mathcal{D}_\alpha \neq \emptyset$ for all $\alpha < \lambda$ and $\mathcal{G} \cap \mathcal{E}_n \neq \emptyset$ for all $n \in \omega$. Let $C = \cup\{s \mid \exists p = (s, \mathcal{T}_0) \in \mathcal{G}\}$. It is straightforward to show that C is infinite and for all $\alpha < \lambda(C \subseteq^* T_\alpha)$. Therefore, $\mathcal{T}$ is not maximal. $\qquad \square$

Problem Set 15

LEVEL 1

1. Show that there are exactly two monoids on the set $S = \{e, a\}$, where e is the identity. Which of these monoids are groups? Which of these monoids are commutative?

Solution: Let's let e be the identity. Since $e \star x = x \star e = x$ for all x in the monoid, we can easily fill out the first row and the first column of the table.

$\star$	e	a
e	e	a
a	a	$\boxdot$

The entry labeled with $\boxdot$ must be either e or a because we need $\star$ to be a binary operation on S.

Case 1: If we let $\boxdot$ be a, we get the following table.

$\star$	e	a
e	e	a
a	a	a

Associativity holds because any computation of the form $(x \star y) \star z$ or $x \star (y \star z)$ will result in a if any of x, y, or z is a. So, all that is left to check is that $(e \star e) \star e = e \star (e \star e)$. But each side of that equation is equal to e.

So, with this multiplication table, $(S, \star)$ **is** a monoid.

This monoid is **not** a group because a has no inverse. Indeed, $a \star e = a \neq e$ and $a \star a = a \neq e$.

This monoid **is** commutative because $a \star e = a$ and $e \star a = a$.

Case 2: If we let $\boxdot$ be e, we get the following table.

$\star$	e	a
e	e	a
a	a	e

Let's check that associativity holds. There are eight instances to check.

$$(e \star e) \star e = e \star e = e \qquad e \star (e \star e) = e \star e = e$$
$$(e \star e) \star a = e \star a = a \qquad e \star (e \star a) = e \star a = a$$
$$(e \star a) \star e = a \star e = a \qquad e \star (a \star e) = e \star a = a$$
$$(a \star e) \star e = a \star e = a \qquad a \star (e \star e) = a \star e = a$$
$$(e \star a) \star a = a \star a = e \qquad e \star (a \star a) = e \star e = e$$
$$(a \star e) \star a = a \star a = e \qquad a \star (e \star a) = a \star a = e$$
$$(a \star a) \star e = e \star e = e \qquad a \star (a \star e) = a \star a = e$$
$$(a \star a) \star a = e \star a = a \qquad a \star (a \star a) = a \star e = a$$

So, with this multiplication table, $(S, \star)$ **is** a monoid.

86

Since $e \star e = e$, e is its own inverse. Since $a \star a = e$, a is also its own inverse. Therefore, each element of this monoid is invertible. It follows that this monoid **is** a group.

This monoid **is** commutative because $a \star e = a$ and $e \star a = a$.

2. The addition and multiplication tables below are defined on the set $S = \{0, 1\}$. Show that $(S, +, \cdot)$ does **not** define a ring.

+	0	1
0	0	1
1	1	0

$\cdot$	0	1
0	1	0
1	0	1

Solution: We have $0(1 + 1) = 0 \cdot 0 = 1$ and $0 \cdot 1 + 0 \cdot 1 = 0 + 0 = 0$. So, $0(1 + 1) \neq 0 \cdot 1 + 0 \cdot 1$. Therefore, multiplication is **not** distributive over addition in S, and so, $(S, +, \cdot)$ does not define a ring.

Notes: (1) Both multiplication tables given are the same, except that we interchanged the roles of 0 and 1 (in technical terms, $(S, +)$ and $(S, \cdot)$ are **isomorphic**).

Both tables represent the unique table for a group with 2 elements. See Problem 1 above for details.

(2) Since $(S, +)$ is a commutative group and $(S, \cdot)$ is a monoid (in fact, it's a commutative group), we know that the only possible way $(S, +, \cdot)$ can fail to be a ring is for distributivity to fail.

3. The addition and multiplication tables below are defined on the set $S = \{0, 1, 2\}$. Show that $(S, +, \cdot)$ does **not** define a field.

+	0	1	2
0	0	1	2
1	1	2	0
2	2	0	1

$\cdot$	0	1	2
0	0	0	0
1	0	1	2
2	0	2	2

Solution: We have $2 \cdot 0 = 0$, $2 \cdot 1 = 2$, and $2 \cdot 2 = 2$. So, 2 has no multiplicative inverse, and therefore, $(S, +, \cdot)$ does **not** define a field.

Note: It's not difficult to check that $(S, +)$ is a group with identity 0 and $(S, \cdot)$ is a monoid with identity 1. However, $(S, +, \cdot)$ is not a ring, as distributivity fails. Here is a counterexample:

$$2(1 + 1) = 2 \cdot 2 = 2 \qquad 2 \cdot 1 + 2 \cdot 1 = 2 + 2 = 1$$

We could have used this computation to verify that $(S, +, \cdot)$ is not a field.

4. Let $F = \{0, 1\}$, where $0 \neq 1$. Show that there is exactly one field $(F, +, \cdot)$, where 0 is the additive identity and 1 is the multiplicative identity.

Solution: Suppose that $(F, +, \cdot)$ is a field. Since $(F, +)$ is a commutative group, by Problem 1 above, the addition table must be the following.

$$
\begin{array}{c|cc}
+ & 0 & 1 \\
\hline
0 & 0 & 1 \\
1 & 1 & 0 \\
\end{array}
$$

Since $(F^*, \cdot)$ is a monoid and 1 is the multiplicative identity, we must have $1 \cdot 1 = 1$.

Now, if $0 \cdot 0 = 1$, then we have $1 = 0 \cdot 0 = 0(0 + 0) = 0 \cdot 0 + 0 \cdot 0 = 1 + 1 = 0$, a contradiction. So, $0 \cdot 0 = 0$.

If $0 \cdot 1 = 1$, then we have $1 = 0 \cdot 1 = (0 + 0) \cdot 1 = 0 \cdot 1 + 0 \cdot 1 = 1 + 1 = 0$, a contradiction. So, $0 \cdot 1 = 0$.

Finally, if $1 \cdot 0 = 1$, then we have $1 = 1 \cdot 0 = 1(0 + 0) = 1 \cdot 0 + 1 \cdot 0 = 1 + 1 = 0$, a contradiction. So, $1 \cdot 0 = 0$.

It follows that the addition and multiplication tables must be as follows:

$$
\begin{array}{c|cc}
+ & 0 & 1 \\
\hline
0 & 0 & 1 \\
1 & 1 & 0 \\
\end{array}
\qquad
\begin{array}{c|cc}
\cdot & 0 & 1 \\
\hline
0 & 0 & 0 \\
1 & 0 & 1 \\
\end{array}
$$

Since we already know that $(F, +)$ is a commutative group and $(F^*, \cdot)$ is a monoid, all we need to verify is that distributivity and the multiplicative inverse property hold. Since $\cdot$ is commutative for S (by Problem 1 above), it suffices to verify left distributivity. We will do this by brute force. There are eight instances to check.

$$
\begin{array}{ll}
0(0 + 0) = 0 \cdot 0 = 0 & 0 \cdot 0 + 0 \cdot 0 = 0 + 0 = 0 \\
0(0 + 1) = 0 \cdot 1 = 0 & 0 \cdot 0 + 0 \cdot 1 = 0 + 0 = 0 \\
0(1 + 0) = 0 \cdot 1 = 0 & 0 \cdot 1 + 0 \cdot 0 = 0 + 0 = 0 \\
0(1 + 1) = 0 \cdot 0 = 0 & 0 \cdot 1 + 0 \cdot 1 = 0 + 0 = 0 \\
1(0 + 0) = 1 \cdot 0 = 0 & 1 \cdot 0 + 1 \cdot 0 = 0 + 0 = 0 \\
1(0 + 1) = 1 \cdot 1 = 1 & 1 \cdot 0 + 1 \cdot 1 = 0 + 1 = 1 \\
1(1 + 0) = 1 \cdot 1 = 1 & 1 \cdot 1 + 1 \cdot 0 = 1 + 0 = 1 \\
1(1 + 1) = 1 \cdot 0 = 0 & 1 \cdot 1 + 1 \cdot 1 = 1 + 1 = 0 \\
\end{array}
$$

So, we see that left distributivity holds, and therefore $(S, +, \cdot)$ is a commutative ring.

Since $1 \cdot 1 = 1$, the multiplicative inverse property holds, and it follows that $(F, +, \cdot)$ is a field.

LEVEL 2

5. Let $G = \{e, a, b\}$ and let $(G, \star)$ be a group with identity element e. Draw a multiplication table for $(G, \star)$.

Solution: Since $e \star x = x \star e = x$ for all x in the group, we can easily fill out the first row and the first column of the table.

$$
\begin{array}{c|ccc}
\star & e & a & b \\
\hline
e & e & a & b \\
a & a & \boxed{\cdot} & \\
b & b & & \\
\end{array}
$$

88

Now, the entry labeled with $\boxdot$ must be either e or b because a is already in that row. If it were e, then the final entry in the row would be b giving two b's in the last column. Therefore, the entry labeled with $\boxdot$ must be b.

$\star$	e	a	b
e	e	a	b
a	a	b	
b	b		

Since the same element cannot be repeated in any row or column, the rest of the table is now determined.

$\star$	e	a	b
e	e	a	b
a	a	b	e
b	b	e	a

Notes: (1) Why can't the same element appear twice in any row? Well if x appeared twice in the row corresponding to y, that would mean that there are elements z and w with $z \neq w$ such that $y \star z = x$ and $y \star w = x$. So, $y \star z = y \star w$. We can multiply each side of the equation on the left by y^{-1} (the inverse of y) to get $y^{-1} \star (y \star z) = y^{-1} \star (y \star w)$. By associativity, $(y^{-1} \star y) \star z = (y^{-1} \star y) \star w$. Now, $y^{-1} \star y = e$ by the inverse property. So, we have $e \star z = e \star w$. Finally, since e is an identity, $z = w$. This contradiction establishes that no element x can appear twice in the same row of a group multiplication table.

A similar argument can be used to show that the same element cannot appear twice in any column.

(2) The argument given in Note 1 used all the group properties (associativity, identity, and inverse). What if we remove one of the properties. For example, what about the multiplication table for a monoid? Can an element appear twice in a row or column? I leave this as an optional exercise.

(3) In Note 1 above, we showed that in the multiplication table for a group, the same element cannot appear as the output more than once in any row or column. We can also show that every element must appear in every row and column. Let's show that the element y must appear in the row corresponding to x. We are looking for an element z such that $x \star z = y$. Well, $z = x^{-1} \star y$ works. Indeed, we have $x \star (x^{-1} \star y) = (x \star x^{-1}) \star y = e \star y = y$.

(4) Using Notes 1 and 3, we see that each element of a group appears exactly once in every row and column of the group's multiplication table.

(5) We have shown that there is essentially just one group of size 3, namely the one given by the table that we produced. Any other group with 3 elements will look exactly like this one, except for possibly the names of the elements. In technical terms, we say that any two groups of order 3 are **isomorphic**.

(6) Observe that in the table we produced, $b = a \star a$. We will generally abbreviate $a \star a$ as a^2. So, another way to draw the table is as follows:

$\star$	e	a	a^2
e	e	a	a^2
a	a	a^2	e
a^2	a^2	e	a

This group is the **cyclic group of order 3**. We call it **cyclic** because the group consists of all powers of the single element a (the elements are a, a^2, and $a^3 = a^0 = e$). The **order** is the number of elements in the group.

6. Prove that in any monoid $(M,\star)$, the identity element is unique.

Proof: Let $(M,\star)$ be a monoid and suppose that e and f are both identity elements in M. Then, we have $f = e \star f = e$. Since we have shown f and e to be equal, there is only one identity element. $\quad\square$

Notes: (1) The word "unique" means that there is only one. In mathematics, we often show that an object is unique by starting with two such objects and then arguing that they must actually be the same. Notice that in the proof above, when we said that e and f are both identity elements, we never insisted that they be *distinct* identity elements. And in fact, the end of the argument shows that they are not distinct.

(2) $e \star f = f$ because e is an identity element and $e \star f = e$ because f is an identity element.

7. Let $(F, +, \cdot)$ be a field. Prove each of the following:

    (i)   If $a, b \in F$ with $a + b = b$, then $a = 0$.

    (ii)   If $a \in F$, $b \in F^*$, and $ab = b$, then $a = 1$.

    (iii) If $a \in F$, then $a \cdot 0 = 0$.

    (iv) If $a \in F^*$, $b \in F$, and $ab = 1$, then $b = \frac{1}{a}$.

    (v)   If $a, b \in F$ and $ab = 0$, then $a = 0$ or $b = 0$.

    (vi) If $a \in F$, then $-a = -1a$.

    (vii) $(-1)(-1) = 1$.

Proofs:

    (i)   Let $a, b \in F$ with $a + b = b$. Then we have
$$a = a + 0 = a + \big(b + (-b)\big) = (a + b) + (-b) = b + (-b) = 0. \qquad\square$$

    (ii)   Let $a \in F$, $b \in F^*$, and $ab = b$. Then we have
$$a = a \cdot 1 = a(bb^{-1}) = (ab)b^{-1} = bb^{-1} = 1. \qquad\square$$

    (iii) Let $a \in F$. Then $a \cdot 0 + a = a \cdot 0 + a \cdot 1 = a(0 + 1) = a \cdot 1 = a$. By (i), $a \cdot 0 = 0$. $\quad\square$

    (iv) Let $a \in F^*$, $b \in F$, and $ab = 1$. Then $b = 1b = (a^{-1}a)b = a^{-1}(ab) = a^{-1} \cdot 1 = a^{-1} = \frac{1}{a}.\square$

    (v)   Let $a, b \in F$ and $ab = 0$. Assume that $a \neq 0$. Then $b = 1b = (a^{-1}a)b = a^{-1}(ab) = a^{-1} \cdot 0$.
         By (iii), $a^{-1} \cdot 0 = 0$. So, $b = 0$. $\quad\square$

(vi)   Let $a \in F$. Then $-1a + a = a(-1) + a \cdot 1 = a(-1 + 1) = a \cdot 0 = 0$ (by (iii)). So, $-1a$ is the additive inverse of a. Thus, $-1a = -a$. □

(vii) $(-1)(-1) + (-1) = (-1)(-1) + (-1) \cdot 1 = (-1)(-1 + 1) = (-1)(0) = 0$ (by (iii)). So, we see that $(-1)(-1)$ is the additive inverse of -1. Therefore, $(-1)(-1) = -(-1)$. □

---

8. Let $(F, +, \cdot)$ be a field with $\mathbb{N} \subseteq F$. Prove that $\mathbb{Q} \subseteq F$.

Proof: Let $n \in \mathbb{Z}$. If $n \in \mathbb{N}$, then $n \in F$ because $\mathbb{N} \subseteq F$. If $n \notin \mathbb{N}$, then $-n \in \mathbb{N}$. So, $-n \in F$. Since F is a field, we have $n = -(-n) \in F$. For each $n \in \mathbb{Z}^*$, $\frac{1}{n} = n^{-1} \in F$ because $n \in F$ and the multiplicative inverse property holds in F. Now, let $\frac{m}{n} \in \mathbb{Q}$. Then $m \in \mathbb{Z}$ and $n \in \mathbb{Z}^*$. Since $\mathbb{Z} \subseteq F$, $m \in F$. Since $n \in \mathbb{Z}^*$, we have $\frac{1}{n} \in F$. Therefore, $\frac{m}{n} = \frac{m \cdot 1}{1 \cdot n} = \frac{m}{1} \cdot \frac{1}{n} = m\left(\frac{1}{n}\right) \in F$ because F is closed under multiplication. Since $\frac{m}{n}$ was an arbitrary element of $\mathbb{Q}$, we see that $\mathbb{Q} \subseteq F$. □

LEVEL 3

9. Assume that a group $(G, \star)$ of order 4 exists with $G = \{e, a, b, c\}$, where e is the identity, $a^2 = b$ and $b^2 = e$. Construct the table for the operation of such a group.

Solution: Since $e \star x = x \star e = x$ for all x in the group, we can easily fill out the first row and the first column of the table.

$\star$	e	a	b	c
e	e	a	b	c
a	a			
b	b			
c	c			

We now add in $a \star a = a^2 = b$ and $b \star b = b^2 = e$.

$\star$	e	a	b	c
e	e	a	b	c
a	a	b	$\boxdot$	
b	b		e	
c	c			

Now, the entry labeled with $\boxdot$ cannot be a or b because a and b appear in that row. It also cannot be e because e appears in that column. Therefore, the entry labeled with $\boxdot$ must be c. It follows that the entry to the right of $\boxdot$ must be e, and the entry at the bottom of the column must be a.

$\star$	e	a	b	c
e	e	a	b	c
a	a	b	c	e
b	b	$\odot$	e	
c	c		a	

Now, the entry labeled with $\odot$ cannot be b or e because b and e appear in that row. It also cannot be a because a appears in that column. Therefore, the entry labeled with $\odot$ must be c. The rest of the table is then determined.

$\star$	e	a	b	c
e	e	a	b	c
a	a	b	c	e
b	b	c	e	a
c	c	e	a	b

Note: Observe that in the table we produced, $b = a \star a = a^2$ and $c = b \star a = a^2 \star a = a^3$. So, another way to draw the table is as follows:

$\star$	e	a	a^2	a^3
e	e	a	a^2	a^3
a	a	a^2	a^3	e
a^2	a^2	a^3	e	a
a^3	a^3	e	a	a^2

This group is the **cyclic group of order 4**.

10. Prove that in any group $(G, \star)$, each element has a unique inverse.

Proof: Let $a \in G$ and suppose that $b, c \in G$ are both inverses of a. We will show that b and c must be the same. We have $c = c \star e = c \star (a \star b) = (c \star a) \star b = e \star b = b$. $\qquad \square$

Notes: (1) $c = c \star e$ because e is an identity element.

(2) $e = a \star b$ because b is an inverse of a. So, $c \star e = c \star (a \star b)$.

(3) $c \star (a \star b) = (c \star a) \star b$ by associativity of $\star$.

(4) $c \star a = e$ because c is an inverse of a. So, $(c \star a) \star b = e \star b$.

(5) $e \star b = b$ because e is an identity element.

11. Let $(F, +, \cdot, \leq)$ be an ordered field. Prove each of the following:

    (i)   If $a, b \in F^+$ and $a > b$, then $\frac{1}{a} < \frac{1}{b}$.

    (ii)   If $a, b \in F$, then $a \geq b$ if and only if $-a \leq -b$.

Proofs:

    (i)   Let $a, b \in F^+$ and $a > b$. Then $a - b = a + (-b) > b + (-b) = 0$ (we used Order Property 1 here). So, $\frac{1}{b} - \frac{1}{a} = \frac{1}{ab}(a - b)$. Since $a, b \in F^+$, $ab \in F^+$ by Order Property (2). So, $\frac{1}{ab} \in F^+$ by Theorem 15.3. Since $\frac{1}{ab} > 0$ and $a - b > 0$, we have $\frac{1}{b} - \frac{1}{a} = \frac{1}{ab}(a - b) > 0$. So, $\frac{1}{b} > \frac{1}{a}$, or equivalently, $\frac{1}{a} < \frac{1}{b}$. $\qquad \square$

(ii)   Let $a, b \in F$. Then $a \geq b$ if and only if $a - b \geq 0$ if and only if $-(a - b) \leq 0$ if and only if $-1(a + (-b)) \leq 0$ if and only if $-1a - 1(-b) \leq 0$ if and only if $-a - (-b) \leq 0$ if and only if $-a < -b$.   □

12. Let $(F, +, \cdot)$ be a field. Show that $(F, \cdot)$ is a commutative monoid.

Proof: Let $(F, +, \cdot)$ be a field. Then $\cdot$ is a binary operation on F and $(F^*, \cdot)$ is a commutative group.

We first show that if $a \in F$, then $0a = 0$. To see this, observe that

$$0a + a = 0a + 1a = (0 + 1)a = 1a = a.$$

By Problem 7, part (i), $0a = 0$.

Let $x, y \in F$. If $x, y \in F^*$, then $xy = yx$. If $x = 0$, then $xy = 0y = 0$ by the previous result, and $yx = y \cdot 0 = 0$ by Problem 7, part (iii) above. If $y = 0$, then $xy = x \cdot 0 = 0$ by Problem 7, part (iii) above, and $yx = 0x = 0$ by the previous result. In all cases, we have $xy = yx$.

Next, let $x, y, z \in F$. If $x, y, z \in F^*$, then $(xy)z = x(yz)$. If $x = 0$, then by the previous result, we have $(xy)z = (0y)z = 0z = 0$ and $x(yz) = 0(yz) = 0$. If $y = 0$, by Problem 7, part (iii) and the previous result, we have $(xy)z = (x \cdot 0)z = 0z = 0$ and $x(yz) = x(0z) = x \cdot 0 = 0$. If $z = 0$, we have $(xy)z = (xy) \cdot 0 = 0$ and $x(yz) = x(y \cdot 0) = x \cdot 0 = 0$. In all cases, we have $(xy)z = x(yz)$.

Let $x \in F$. If $x \in F^*$, then $1x = x \cdot 1 = x$. If $x = 0$, then by Problem 7, part (iii), $1x = 1 \cdot 0 = 0$ and by the previous result, $x \cdot 1 = 0 \cdot 1 = 0$. In all cases, we have $1x = x \cdot 1 = x$.

Therefore, $(F, \cdot)$ is a commutative monoid.   □

LEVEL 4

13. Let $(G, \star)$ be a group with $a, b \in G$, and let a^{-1} and b^{-1} be the inverses of a and b, respectively. Prove

(i) $(a \star b)^{-1} = b^{-1} \star a^{-1}$.

(ii)   the inverse of a^{-1} is a.

Proof of (i): Let $a, b \in G$. Then we have

$$(a \star b) \star (b^{-1} \star a^{-1}) = a \star \left(b \star (b^{-1} \star a^{-1})\right) = a \star \left((b \star b^{-1}) \star a^{-1}\right) = a \star (e \star a^{-1}) = a \star a^{-1} = e$$

and

$$(b^{-1} \star a^{-1}) \star (a \star b) = b^{-1} \star \left(a^{-1} \star (a \star b)\right) = b^{-1} \star \left((a^{-1} \star a) \star b\right) = b^{-1} \star (e \star b) = b^{-1} \star b = e.$$

So, $(a \star b)^{-1} = (b^{-1} \star a^{-1})$.   □

Notes: (1) For the first and second equalities we used the associativity of $\star$ in G.

(2) For the third equality, we used the inverse property of $\star$ in G.

(3) For the fourth equality, we used the identity property of $\star$ in G.

(4) For the last equality, we again used the inverse property of $\star$ in G.

(5) Since multiplying $a \star b$ on either side by $b^{-1} \star a^{-1}$ results in the identity element e, it follows that $b^{-1} \star a^{-1}$ is the inverse of $a \star b$.

(6) In a group, to verify that an element h is the inverse of an element g, it suffices to show that $g \star h = e$ **or** $h \star g = e$. In other words, we can prove that $g \star h = e \to h \star g = e$ and we can prove that $h \star g = e \to g \star h = e$.

For a proof that $g \star h = e \to h \star g = e$, suppose that $g \star h = e$ and k is the inverse of g. Then $g \star k = k \star g = e$. Since $g \star h = e$ and $g \star k = e$, we have $g \star h = g \star k$. By multiplying by g^{-1} on each side of this equation, and using associativity, the inverse property, and the identity property, we get $h = k$. So, h is in fact the inverse of g.

Proving that $h \star g = e \to g \star h = e$ is similar. Thus, in the solution above, we need only show one of the sequences of equalities given. The second one follows for free.

Proof of (ii): Let $a \in G$. Since a^{-1} is the inverse of a, we have $a \star a^{-1} = a^{-1} \star a = e$. But this sequence of equations also says that a is the inverse of a^{-1}. □

14. Prove that there is no smallest positive real number.

Proof: Let $x \in \mathbb{R}^+$ and let $y = \frac{1}{2}x$. By Theorem 15.3, $\frac{1}{2} > 0$. So, by Order Property (2), $y > 0$.

Now, $x - y = x - \frac{1}{2}x = 1x - \frac{1}{2}x = \left(1 - \frac{1}{2}\right)x = \left(\frac{2}{2} - \frac{1}{2}\right)x = \frac{1}{2}x > 0$. So, $x > y$. It follows that y is a positive real number smaller than x. Since x was an arbitrary positive real number, there is no smallest positive real number. □

15. Let a be a nonnegative real number. Prove that $a = 0$ if and only if a is less than every positive real number. (Note: a nonnegative means $a \geq 0$.)

Proof: Let a be a nonnegative real number.

First suppose that $a = 0$. Let ϵ be a positive real number, so that $\epsilon > 0$. Then by direct substitution, $\epsilon > a$, or equivalently $a < \epsilon$. Since ϵ was an arbitrary positive real number, we have shown that a is less than every positive real number.

Now, suppose that a is less than every positive real number. Assume towards contradiction that $a \neq 0$. Then $a > 0$ (because a is nonnegative). Let $\epsilon = \frac{1}{2}a$. By the same reasoning used in Problem 14 above, we have that ϵ is a positive real number with $a > \epsilon$. This contradicts our assumption that a is less than every positive real number. □

16. Prove that every rational number can be written in the form $\frac{m}{n}$, where $m \in \mathbb{Z}$, $n \in \mathbb{Z}^*$, and at least one of m or n is **not** even.

94

Proof: Let x be a rational number. Then there are $a \in \mathbb{Z}$ and $b \in \mathbb{Z}^*$ such that $x = \frac{a}{b}$. Let j be the largest integer such that 2^j divides a and let k be the largest integer such that 2^k divides b. Since, 2^j divides a, there is $c \in \mathbb{Z}$ such that $a = 2^j c$. Since, 2^k divides b, there is $d \in \mathbb{Z}$ such that $b = 2^k d$.

Observe that c is odd. Indeed, if c were even, then there would be an integer s such that $c = 2s$. But then $a = 2^j c = 2^j(2s) = (2^j \cdot 2)s = (2^j \cdot 2^1)s = 2^{j+1}s$. So, 2^{j+1} divides a, contradicting the maximality of j.

Similarly, d is odd.

So, we have $x = \frac{a}{b} = \frac{2^j c}{2^k d}$.

If $j \geq k$, then, $j - k \geq 0$ and $x = \frac{2^j c}{2^k d} = \frac{2^{j-k}c}{d}$. Let $m = 2^{j-k}c$ and $n = d$. Then $x = \frac{m}{n}$, $m \in \mathbb{Z}$ (because $\mathbb{Z}$ is closed under multiplication), $n \in \mathbb{Z}^*$ (if $n = 0$, then $b = 2^k d = 2^k n = 2^k \cdot 0 = 0$), and $n = d$ is odd.

If $j < k$, then $k - j > 0$ and $x = \frac{2^j c}{2^k d} = \frac{c}{2^{k-j}d}$. Let $m = c$ and $n = 2^{k-j}d$. Then $x = \frac{m}{n}$, $m = c \in \mathbb{Z}$, $n \in \mathbb{Z}^*$ (because $\mathbb{Z}$ is closed under multiplication, and if n were 0, then d would be 0, and then b would be 0), and $m = c$ is odd. $\qquad\square$

LEVEL 5

17. Prove that $(\mathbb{Q}, +, \cdot, \leq)$ and $(\mathbb{R}, +, \cdot, \leq)$ are ordered fields.

Proof: We first prove that $(\mathbb{Q}, +)$ is a commutative group.

(Closure) Let $x, y \in \mathbb{Q}$. Then there exist $a, c \in \mathbb{Z}$ and $b, d \in \mathbb{Z}^*$ such that $x = \frac{a}{b}$ and $y = \frac{c}{d}$. We have $x + y = \frac{a}{b} + \frac{c}{d} = \frac{ad+bc}{bd}$. Since $\mathbb{Z}$ is closed under multiplication, $ad \in \mathbb{Z}$ and $bc \in \mathbb{Z}$. Since $\mathbb{Z}$ is closed under addition, $ad + bc \in \mathbb{Z}$. Since $\mathbb{Z}^*$ is closed under multiplication, $bd \in \mathbb{Z}^*$. Therefore, $x + y \in \mathbb{Q}$.

(Associativity) Let $x, y, z \in \mathbb{Q}$. Then there exist $a, c, e \in \mathbb{Z}$ and $b, d, f \in \mathbb{Z}^*$ such that $x = \frac{a}{b}$, $y = \frac{c}{d}$, and $z = \frac{e}{f}$. Since multiplication and addition are associative in $\mathbb{Z}$, multiplication is (both left and right) distributive over addition in $\mathbb{Z}$ (see the Note below), and multiplication is associative in $\mathbb{Z}^*$, we have

$$(x + y) + z = \left(\frac{a}{b} + \frac{c}{d}\right) + \frac{e}{f} = \frac{ad + bc}{bd} + \frac{e}{f} = \frac{(ad + bc)f + (bd)e}{(bd)f} = \frac{((ad)f + (bc)f) + (bd)e}{(bd)f}$$

$$= \frac{a(df) + (b(cf) + b(de))}{b(df)} = \frac{a(df) + b(cf + de)}{b(df)} = \frac{a}{b} + \frac{cf + de}{df} = \frac{a}{b} + \left(\frac{c}{d} + \frac{e}{f}\right) = x + (y + z).$$

(Identity) Let $\overline{0} = \frac{0}{1}$. We show that $\overline{0}$ is an identity for $(\mathbb{Q}, +)$. Let $x \in \mathbb{Q}$. Then there exist $a \in \mathbb{Z}$ and $b \in \mathbb{Z}^*$ such that $x = \frac{a}{b}$. Since 0 is an identity for $\mathbb{Z}$, and $0 \cdot x = x \cdot 0 = 0$ for all $x \in \mathbb{Z}$, we have

$$x + \overline{0} = \frac{a}{b} + \frac{0}{1} = \frac{a \cdot 1 + b \cdot 0}{b \cdot 1} = \frac{a + 0}{b} = \frac{a}{b} = x \text{ and } \overline{0} + x = \frac{0}{1} + \frac{a}{b} = \frac{0b + 1a}{1b} = \frac{0 + a}{b} = \frac{a}{b} = x.$$

(Inverse) Let $x \in \mathbb{Q}$. Then there exist $a \in \mathbb{Z}$ and $b \in \mathbb{Z}^*$ such that $x = \frac{a}{b}$. Let $y = \frac{-1a}{b}$. Since $\mathbb{Z}$ is closed under multiplication, $-1a \in \mathbb{Z}$. So, $y \in \mathbb{Q}$. Since multiplication is associative and commutative in $\mathbb{Z}$ and $(-1)n = -n$ for all $n \in \mathbb{Z}$, we have

$$x + y = \frac{a}{b} + \frac{-1a}{b} = \frac{ab + b(-1a)}{b \cdot b} = \frac{ab + (-1a)b}{b^2} = \frac{ab + (-1)(ab)}{b^2} = \frac{ab - ab}{b^2} = \frac{0}{b^2} = \overline{0}$$

$$y + x = \frac{-1a}{b} + \frac{a}{b} = \frac{(-1a)b + ba}{b \cdot b} = \frac{-1(ab) + ab}{b^2} = \frac{-ab + ab}{b^2} = \frac{0}{b^2} = \overline{0}$$

So, y is the additive inverse of x.

(Commutativity) Let $x, y \in \mathbb{Q}$. Then there exist $a, c \in \mathbb{Z}$ and $b, d \in \mathbb{Z}^*$ such that $x = \frac{a}{b}$ and $y = \frac{c}{d}$. Since multiplication and addition are commutative in $\mathbb{Z}$, and multiplication is commutative in $\mathbb{Z}^*$, we have

$$x + y = \frac{a}{b} + \frac{c}{d} = \frac{ad + bc}{bd} = \frac{bc + ad}{db} = \frac{cb + da}{db} = \frac{c}{d} + \frac{a}{b} = y + x.$$

So, $(\mathbb{Q}, +)$ is a commutative group.

We next prove that $(\mathbb{Q} \setminus \{0\}, \cdot)$ is a commutative group.

(Closure) Let $x, y \in \mathbb{Q}^*$. Then there exist $a, b, c, d \in \mathbb{Z}^*$ such that $x = \frac{a}{b}$ and $y = \frac{c}{d}$. We have $xy = \frac{a}{b} \cdot \frac{c}{d} = \frac{ac}{bd}$. Since $\mathbb{Z}^*$ is closed under multiplication, $ac, bd \in \mathbb{Z}^*$. Therefore, $xy \in \mathbb{Q}^*$.

(Associativity) Let $x, y, z \in \mathbb{Q}^*$. Then there exist $a, b, c, d, e, f \in \mathbb{Z}^*$ such that $x = \frac{a}{b}$, $y = \frac{c}{d}$, and $z = \frac{e}{f}$. Since multiplication is associative in $\mathbb{Z}^*$, we have

$$(xy)z = \left(\frac{a}{b} \cdot \frac{c}{d}\right)\frac{e}{f} = \left(\frac{ac}{bd}\right)\frac{e}{f} = \frac{(ac)e}{(bd)f} = \frac{a(ce)}{b(df)} = \frac{a}{b}\left(\frac{ce}{df}\right) = \frac{a}{b}\left(\frac{c}{d} \cdot \frac{e}{f}\right) = x(yz).$$

(Identity) Let $\overline{1} = \frac{1}{1}$. We show that $\overline{1}$ is an identity for $(\mathbb{Q}^*, \cdot)$. Let $x \in \mathbb{Q}^*$. Then there exist $a, b \in \mathbb{Z}^*$ such that $x = \frac{a}{b}$. Since 1 is an identity for $\mathbb{Z}^*$, we have

$$x \cdot \overline{1} = \frac{a}{b} \cdot \frac{1}{1} = \frac{a \cdot 1}{b \cdot 1} = \frac{a}{b} = x \text{ and } \overline{1}x = \frac{1}{1} \cdot \frac{a}{b} = \frac{1a}{1b} = \frac{a}{b} = x.$$

(Inverse) Let $x \in \mathbb{Q}^*$. Then there exist $a, b \in \mathbb{Z}^*$ such that $x = \frac{a}{b}$. Let $y = \frac{b}{a}$. Then $y \in \mathbb{Q}^*$ (note that $a \neq 0$). Since multiplication is commutative in $\mathbb{Z}^*$, we have

$$xy = \frac{a}{b} \cdot \frac{b}{a} = \frac{ab}{ba} = \frac{ab}{ab} = \frac{1}{1} = \overline{1}.$$

So, y is the multiplicative inverse of x.

(Commutativity) Let $x, y \in \mathbb{Q}^*$. Then there exist $a, b, c, d \in \mathbb{Z}^*$ such that $x = \frac{a}{b}$ and $y = \frac{c}{d}$. Since multiplication is commutative in $\mathbb{Z}^*$, we have

$$xy = \frac{a}{b} \cdot \frac{c}{d} = \frac{ac}{bd} = \frac{ca}{db} = \frac{c}{d} \cdot \frac{a}{b} = yx.$$

So, $(\mathbb{Q}^*, \cdot)$ is a commutative group.

Now we prove that multiplication is distributive over addition in $\mathbb{Q}$.

(Distributivity) Let $x, y, z \in \mathbb{Q}$. Then there exist $a, c, e \in \mathbb{Z}$ and $b, d, f \in \mathbb{Z}^*$ such that $x = \frac{a}{b}, y = \frac{c}{d}$, and $z = \frac{e}{f}$. Let's start with left distributivity.

$$x(y + z) = \frac{a}{b}\left(\frac{c}{d} + \frac{e}{f}\right) = \frac{a}{b}\left(\frac{cf + de}{df}\right) = \frac{a(cf + de)}{b(df)}$$

$$xy + xz = \frac{a}{b} \cdot \frac{c}{d} + \frac{a}{b} \cdot \frac{e}{f} = \frac{ac}{bd} + \frac{ae}{bf} = \frac{(ac)(bf) + (bd)(ae)}{(bd)(bf)}$$

We need to verify that $\frac{(ac)(bf)+(bd)(ae)}{(bd)(bf)} = \frac{a(cf+de)}{b(df)}$.

Since $\mathbb{Z}$ is a ring, $(ac)(bf) + (bd)(ae) = bacf + bade = ba(cf + de)$ (see Note 1 below).

Since multiplication is associative and commutative in $\mathbb{Z}^*$, we have

$$(bd)(bf) = b\big(d(bf)\big) = b\big((db)f\big) = b\big((bd)f\big) = b\big(b(df)\big).$$

So, $\frac{(ac)(bf)+(bd)(ae)}{(bd)(bf)} = \frac{ba(cf+de)}{b(b(df))} = \frac{a(cf+de)}{b(df)}$.

For right distributivity, we can use left distributivity together with the commutativity of multiplication in $\mathbb{Q}$.

$$(y + z)x = x(y + z) = xy + xz = yx + zx \qquad \square$$

Notes: (1) We skipped many steps when verifying $(ac)(bf) + (bd)(ae) = ba(cf + de)$. The dedicated reader may want to verify this equality carefully, making sure to use only the fact that $\mathbb{Z}$ is a ring, and making a note of which ring property is being used at each step.

(2) In the very last step of the proof, we cancelled one b in the numerator of the fraction with b in the denominator of the fraction. In general, if $j \in \mathbb{Z}$ and $m, k \in \mathbb{Z}^*$, then $\frac{mj}{mk} = \frac{j}{k}$. To verify that this is true, simply observe that since $\mathbb{Z}$ is a ring, we have $(mj)k = m(jk) = m(kj) = (mk)j$.

We next prove the order properties. Let $\frac{a}{b}, \frac{c}{d}, \frac{e}{f} \in \mathbb{Q}$ and assume that $\frac{a}{b} \leq \frac{c}{d}$. Then $ad \leq bc$. Since $\mathbb{Z}$ is an ordered ring, we get $(af + be)(df) = afdf + bedf = adff + bedf \leq bcff + bedf = bf(cf + de)$. Therefore, $\frac{a}{b} + \frac{e}{f} = \frac{af+be}{bf} \leq \frac{cf+de}{df} = \frac{c}{d} + \frac{e}{f}$.

Next, let $\frac{a}{b}, \frac{c}{d} \in \mathbb{Q}$ with $0 \leq \frac{a}{b}$ and $0 \leq \frac{c}{d}$. We may assume that $a, b, c, d \geq 0$. Then $\frac{a}{b} \cdot \frac{c}{d} = \frac{ac}{bd} \geq 0$.

It follows that $(\mathbb{Q}, +, \cdot, \leq)$ is an ordered field.

We proved that $(\mathbb{R}, +)$ is a commutative group in part 6 of Example 15.3. We next prove that $(\mathbb{Q} \setminus \{0\}, \cdot)$ is a commutative group.

(Closure) This is Problem 11 from Problem Set 6.

(Associativity) To see that $\cdot$ is associative in $\mathbb{R}^*$, we use the associativity of $\cdot$ in $\mathbb{Q}$. If $[(x_n)], [(y_n)], [(z_n)] \in \mathbb{R}^*$, then

$$([(x_n)] \cdot [(y_n)]) \cdot [(z_n)] = [(x_n \cdot y_n)] \cdot [(z_n)] = [((x_n \cdot y_n) \cdot z_n)]$$
$$= [(x_n \cdot (y_n \cdot z_n))] = [x_n] \cdot [(y_n \cdot z_n)] = [(x_n)] \cdot ([(y_n)] \cdot [(z_n)]).$$

(Identity) To see that $[(1)]$ is the multiplicative identity, using the fact that 1 is the additive identity in $\mathbb{Q}$, we have for $[(x_n)] \in \mathbb{R}$,

$$[(1)] \cdot [(x_n)] = [(1 \cdot x_n)] = [(x_n)] \text{ and } [(x_n)] \cdot [(1)] = [(x_n \cdot 1)] = [(x_n)].$$

(Inverse) The inverse of the real number $[(x_n)]$ is $[(y_n)]$, where for each $n \in \mathbb{N}$, $y_n = \frac{1}{x_n}$ if $x_n \neq 0$ and $y_n = 0$ if $x_n = 0$. We have that $[(x_n)] \cdot [(y_n)] = [(z_n)]$ and $[(y_n)] + [(x_n)] = [(z_n)]$, where z_n is 0 or 1 for all $n \in \mathbb{N}$. We claim that $[(z_n)] = [(1)]$. To see this, note that since $[(x_n)] \neq [(0)]$, there is a $K > 0$ such that for $n > N$, $x_n \neq 0$.

(Commutativity) To see that $+$ is commutative in $\mathbb{R}^*$, we use the commutativity of $+$ in $\mathbb{Q}$. If $[(x_n)], [(y_n)] \in \mathbb{R}^*$, then $[(x_n)] + [(y_n)] = [(x_n + y_n)] = [(y_n + x_n)] = [(y_n)] + [(x_n)]$.

(Distributivity) Distributivity is similar to commutativity and associativity.

We next prove the order properties. Let $[(x_n)], [(y_n)], [(z_n)] \in \mathbb{R}$ and assume that $[(x_n)] \leq [(y_n)]$. Then there is $K \in \mathbb{N}$ such that $n > K$ implies $x_n \leq y_n$. Since $\mathbb{Q}$ is an ordered ring, it follows that $n > K$ implies $x_n + z_n \leq y_n + z_n$. So, $[(x_n)] + [(z_n)] = [(x_n + z_n)] \leq [(y_n + z_n)] = [(y_n)] + [(z_n)]$.

Next, let $[(x_n)], [(y_n)] \in \mathbb{R}$ with $[(0)] \leq [(x_n)]$ and $[(0)] \leq [(y_n)]$. Then there is $K_1 \in \mathbb{N}$ such that $n > K_1$ implies $x_n \geq 0$ and there is $K_2 \in \mathbb{N}$ such that $n > K_2$ implies $y_n \geq 0$. Let $K = \max\{K_1, K_2\}$ and let $n > K$. Since $K \geq K_1$, $x_n \geq 0$. Since $K \geq K_2$, $y_n \geq 0$. Since $\mathbb{Q}$ is an ordered ring, $x_n \cdot y_n \geq 0$. Therefore, we have $[(x_n)] \cdot [(y_n)] \geq [(0)]$.

It follows that $(\mathbb{R}, +, \cdot, \leq)$ is an ordered field. $\qquad\qquad\square$

> 18. Prove that every nonempty set of real numbers that is bounded below has a greatest lower bound in $\mathbb{R}$.

Proof: Let S be a nonempty set of real numbers that is bounded below. Let K be a lower bound for S, so that for all $x \in S$, $x \geq K$. Define the set T by $T = \{-x \mid x \in S\}$.

Let $y \in T$. Then there is $x \in S$ with $y = -x$. Since $x \in S$, $x \geq K$. It follows from Problem 11, part (ii) that $y = -x \leq -K$. Since $y \in T$ was arbitrary, we have shown that for all $y \in T$, $y \leq -K$. It follows that $-K$ is an upper bound for the set T.

By the Completeness Property of $\mathbb{R}$, T has a least upper bound M. We will show that $-M$ is a greatest lower bound for S.

Let $x \in S$. Then $-x \in T$. Since M is an upper bound for T, $-x \leq M$. So, by Problem 11, part (ii), $x \geq -M$. Since $x \in S$ was arbitrary, we have shown that for all $x \in S$, $x \geq -M$. Therefore, $-M$ is a lower bound for S.

Let $B > -M$. Then $-B < M$. Since M is the least upper bound for T, there is $y \in T$ with $y > -B$. By Problem 11, part (ii), we have $-y < B$. Since $y \in T$, $-y \in S$. Thus, B is not a lower bound of S.

Therefore, $-M$ is a greatest lower bound for S.

Since S was arbitrary, we have shown that every nonempty set of real numbers that is bounded below has a greatest lower bound in $\mathbb{R}$. $\qquad\square$

19. Show that between any two real numbers there is a real number that is **not** rational.

Proof: Let $x, y \in \mathbb{R}$ with $x < y$. Let c be a positive number that is not rational. Then $\frac{x}{c} < \frac{y}{c}$. By the Density Theorem, there is a $q \in \mathbb{Q}$ such that $\frac{x}{c} < q < \frac{y}{c}$. We can assume that $q \neq 0$ (if it were, we could simply apply the Density Theorem again to get $p \in \mathbb{Q}$ with $\frac{x}{c} < p < q$, and p would not be 0). It follows that $x < cq < y$. Since $c = (cq)q^{-1}$, it follows that $cq \notin \mathbb{Q}$ (if $cq \in \mathbb{Q}$, then $c \in \mathbb{Q}$ because $\mathbb{Q}$ is closed under multiplication). So, cq is a real number between x and y that is **not** rational. $\qquad\square$

20. Let $T = \{x \in F \mid -2 < x \leq 2\}$. Prove $\sup T = 2$ and $\inf T = -2$.

Proof: If $x \in T$, then by the definition of T, $x \leq 2$. So, 2 is an upper bound of T.

Now, let $B < 2$, and let $z = \max\left\{0, \frac{1}{2}(B + 2)\right\}$. Since $B < 2$, we have

$$\frac{1}{2}(B + 2) < \frac{1}{2}(2 + 2) = \frac{1}{2} \cdot 4 = 2.$$

So, if we have $\frac{1}{2}(B + 2) > 0$, then $\frac{1}{2}(B + 2) \in T$. Since $0 \in T$, we see that $z \in T$. Also,

$$z \geq \frac{1}{2}(B + 2) > \frac{1}{2}(B + B) = \frac{1}{2}(2B) = \left(\frac{1}{2} \cdot 2\right)B = 1B = B.$$

So, we see that $z \in T$ and $z > B$. Therefore, B is not an upper bound of T. So, $2 = \sup T$.

If $x \in T$, then by the definition of T, $x > -2$. So, -2 is a lower bound of T.

Now, let $C > -2$, and let $w = \min\left\{0, \frac{1}{2}(-2 + C)\right\}$. Since $C > -2$, we have

$$\frac{1}{2}(-2 + C) > \frac{1}{2}(-2 - 2) = \frac{1}{2}(-4) = -2.$$

So, if we have $\frac{1}{2}(-2 + C) < 0$, then $\frac{1}{2}(-2 + C) \in T$. Since $0 \in T$, we see that $w \in T$. Also,

$$w \leq \frac{1}{2}(-2 + C) < \frac{1}{2}(C + C) = \frac{1}{2}(2C) = \left(\frac{1}{2} \cdot 2\right)C = 1C = C.$$

So, we see that $w \in T$ and $w < C$. Therefore, C is not a lower bound of T. So, $-2 = \inf T$. $\qquad\square$

Problem Set 16

LEVEL 1

1. Let $C = \{\alpha < \omega_1 \mid \alpha$ is a limit ordinal$\}$. Prove that C is a club in ω_1.

Proof: To see that C is unbounded, let $\alpha < \omega_1$. Then $\alpha + \omega$ is a limit ordinal. Also, $\alpha + \omega < \omega_1$ because $|\alpha + \omega| = \max\{|\alpha|, \omega\} = \omega$. To see that C is closed, let $\delta < \omega_1$ be a limit ordinal and suppose that $\{\alpha_\eta \mid \eta < \delta\}$ satisfies (a) for all η, ζ with $\eta < \zeta < \delta$, $\alpha_\eta < \alpha_\zeta$ and (b) for all $\eta < \delta$, α_η is a limit ordinal. Then $\bigcup\{\alpha_\eta \mid \eta < \delta\}$ is a limit ordinal and since ω_1 is regular and $\delta < \kappa$, $\bigcup\{\alpha_\eta \mid \eta < \delta\} < \omega_1$. So, $\bigcup\{\alpha_\eta \mid \eta < \delta\} \in C$. $\qquad\square$

2. Suppose that for each $\alpha < \omega_1$, (i) H_α is a countable DLO, and (ii) for each $\alpha, \beta < \omega_1$, $\alpha < \beta$ implies $H_\alpha \subseteq H_\beta$ and the orderings of H_α and H_β agree on elements of H_α. Let $H = \bigcup\{H_\alpha \mid \alpha < \omega_1\}$. Prove that H is a DLO.

Proof: If $x, y, z \in H$, then there is $\alpha < \omega_1$ such that $x, y, z \in H_\alpha$. If $x < y$ and $y < z$, then $x < z$ because $<$ is transitive in H_α. $x \not< x$ because $<$ is antireflexive in H_α. If $x < y$ and $y < x$, then $x = y$ because $<$ is antisymmetric in H_α. We have $x < y$ or $x = y$, or $y < x$ because trichotomy holds in $(H_\alpha, <)$. There is $z \in H_\alpha$ with $x < z < y$ because density holds in H_α. Since $H_\alpha \subseteq H$, $z \in H$. Similarly, there are $w, t \in H_\alpha$ with $w < x$ and $x < w$ because H_α has no endpoints. Since $H_\alpha \subseteq H$, $w, t \in H$. $\qquad\square$

LEVEL 2

3. Let κ be a regular uncountable cardinal and let C and D be clubs in κ. Prove that $C \cap D$ is a club in κ. Use this result to conclude that every club is a stationary set.

Proof: To see that $C \cap D$ is closed, let $\delta < \kappa$ be a limit ordinal and suppose that $\{\alpha_\eta \mid \eta < \delta\}$ satisfies (a) for all η, ζ with $\eta < \zeta < \delta$, $\alpha_\eta < \alpha_\zeta$ and (b) for all $\eta < \delta$, $\alpha_\eta \in C \cap D$. Let $\alpha = \bigcup\{\alpha_\eta \mid \eta < \delta\}$. Since C is closed, $\alpha \in C$. Since D is closed, $\alpha \in D$. Therefore, $\alpha \in C \cap D$, and so, $C \cap D$ is closed. To see that $C \cap D$ is unbounded, let $\alpha < \kappa$. Let $\alpha_0 > \alpha$ with $\alpha_0 \in C$. Let $\alpha_1 > \alpha_0$ with $\alpha_1 \in D$. In general, for each $n \in \omega$, choose $\alpha_{n+1} > \alpha_n$ with $\alpha_{n+1} \in C$ if n is odd and $\alpha_{n+1} \in D$ if n is even. Then $\alpha_0 < \bigcup\{\alpha_n \mid n < \omega\} < \kappa$ and $\bigcup\{\alpha_n \mid n < \omega\} \in C \cap D$. Therefore, $C \cap D$ is a club in κ.

Now, let C be a club. We need to show that for any club D, $C \cap D \neq \emptyset$. By the result we just proved, $C \cap D$ is a club. In particular, $C \cap D \neq \emptyset$. $\qquad\square$

4. Let κ be a regular uncountable cardinal, let $\lambda < \kappa$ be a cardinal, for each $\alpha < \lambda$, let $C_\alpha \subseteq \kappa$ be a club in κ, and let $C = \bigcap\{C_\alpha \mid \alpha < \lambda\}$. Prove that C is a club in κ.

Proof: To see that C is closed, let $\delta < \kappa$ be a limit ordinal and suppose that $\{\alpha_\eta \mid \eta < \delta\}$ satisfies (a) for all η, ζ with $\eta < \zeta < \delta$, $\alpha_\eta < \alpha_\zeta$ and (b) for all $\eta < \delta$, $\alpha_\eta \in C$. Let $\alpha = \bigcup\{\alpha_\eta \mid \eta < \delta\}$. Let $\beta < \lambda$. Since C_β is closed, $\alpha \in C_\beta$. Since $\beta < \lambda$ was arbitrary, $\alpha \in C$. Therefore, C is closed. To see that C is unbounded, let $\alpha < \kappa$. Let $\alpha_0^0 = \alpha$ and define $\{\alpha_\eta^0 \mid \eta < \lambda\}$ with $\alpha_\eta^0 \in C_\eta$ and for all η, ζ with $\eta < \zeta < \lambda$, $\alpha_\eta^0 < \alpha_\zeta^0$. Let $\alpha_0^1 = \bigcup\{\alpha_\eta^0 \mid \eta < \lambda\}$ and define $\{\alpha_\eta^1 \mid \eta < \lambda\}$ with $\alpha_\eta^1 \in C_\eta$ and for all η, ζ with $\eta < \zeta < \lambda$, $\alpha_\eta^1 < \alpha_\zeta^1$. Let $\alpha_0^2 = \bigcup\{\alpha_\eta^1 \mid \eta < \lambda\}$. In general, for $n < \omega$, let $\alpha_0^{n+1} = \bigcup\{\alpha_\eta^n \mid \eta < \lambda\}$ and define $\{\alpha_\eta^{n+1} \mid \eta < \lambda\}$ with $\alpha_\eta^{n+1} \in C_\eta$ and for all η, ζ with $\eta < \zeta < \lambda$, $\alpha_\eta^{n+1} < \alpha_\zeta^{n+1}$. Let $\alpha_0^{n+2} = \bigcup\{\alpha_\eta^{n+1} \mid \eta < \lambda\}$. Finally, let $\alpha^\omega = \bigcup\{\alpha_0^n \mid n < \omega\}$. Then $\alpha < \alpha^\omega < \kappa$ and for each $\eta < \lambda$, $\alpha^\omega = \bigcup\{\alpha_\eta^n \mid n < \omega\}$. So, for each $\eta < \lambda$, $\alpha^\omega \in C_\eta$. Therefore, $\alpha^\omega \in C$. $\qquad\square$

LEVEL 3

5. Let κ be a regular uncountable cardinal, let $\lambda < \kappa$ be a cardinal, for each $\alpha < \lambda$, let $X_\alpha \subseteq \kappa$ be nonstationary, and let $X = \bigcup\{X_\alpha \mid \alpha < \lambda\}$. Prove that X is nonstationary.

Proof: For each $\alpha < \lambda$, there is a club C_α such that $C_\alpha \cap X_\alpha = \emptyset$. By Problem 4, $C = \bigcap\{C_\alpha \mid \alpha < \lambda\}$ is a club in κ. $C \cap X \subseteq \bigcap\{C_\alpha \cap X_\alpha \mid \alpha < \lambda\}$, and so, $C \cap X = \emptyset$. $\qquad\square$

6. Let κ be a regular uncountable cardinal and let C_η be a club in κ for each $\eta < \kappa$. Prove that $D = \{\eta \mid \forall \beta < \eta (\eta \in C_\beta)\}$ is a club in κ (D is called the **diagonal intersection** of $\{C_\eta \mid \eta < \kappa\}$).

Proof: To see that C is closed, let $\delta < \kappa$ be a limit ordinal and suppose that $\{\alpha_\eta \mid \eta < \delta\}$ satisfies (a) for all η, ζ with $\eta < \zeta < \delta$, $\alpha_\eta < \alpha_\zeta$ and (b) for all $\eta < \delta$, $\alpha_\eta \in D$. Let $\alpha = \bigcup\{\alpha_\eta \mid \eta < \delta\}$. Let $\beta < \alpha$. Then $\beta < \alpha_\eta$ for some $\eta < \delta$. Since $\alpha_\eta \in D$ and $\beta < \alpha_\eta$, we have $\alpha_\eta \in C_\beta$. Since C_β is closed, $\alpha \in C_\beta$. Since $\beta < \alpha$ was arbitrary, $\alpha \in D$. Therefore, D is closed. To see that D is unbounded, for each $\gamma < \kappa$, let $D_\alpha = \bigcap\{C_\alpha \mid \alpha < \gamma\}$. By Problem 4, for each $\alpha < \kappa$, D_α is a club. Now, let $\alpha < \kappa$. Let $\alpha_0^0 = \alpha$ and define $\{\alpha_\eta^0 \mid \eta < \lambda\}$ with $\alpha_\eta^0 \in D_\eta$ and for all η, ζ with $\eta < \zeta < \lambda$, $\alpha_\eta^0 < \alpha_\zeta^0$. Let $\alpha_0^1 = \bigcup\{\alpha_\eta^0 \mid \eta < \lambda\}$ and define $\{\alpha_\eta^1 \mid \eta < \lambda\}$ with $\alpha_\eta^1 \in D_\eta$ and for all η, ζ with $\eta < \zeta < \lambda$, $\alpha_\eta^1 < \alpha_\zeta^1$. Let $\alpha_0^2 = \bigcup\{\alpha_\eta^1 \mid \eta < \lambda\}$, In general, for $n < \omega$, let $\alpha_0^{n+1} = \bigcup\{\alpha_\eta^n \mid \eta < \lambda\}$ and define $\{\alpha_\eta^{n+1} \mid \eta < \lambda\}$ with $\alpha_\eta^{n+1} \in D$ and for all η, ζ with $\eta < \zeta < \lambda$, $\alpha_\eta^{n+1} < \alpha_\zeta^{n+1}$. Let $\alpha_0^{n+2} = \bigcup\{\alpha_\eta^{n+1} \mid \eta < \lambda\}$. Finally, let $\alpha^\omega = \bigcup\{\alpha_0^n \mid n < \omega\}$. Then $\alpha^\omega < \kappa$ and for each $\eta < \lambda$, $\alpha^\omega = \bigcup\{\alpha_\eta^n \mid n < \omega\}$. So, for each $\eta < \lambda$, $\alpha^\omega \in D_\eta$. Thus, $\alpha^\omega \in D$. $\qquad\square$

LEVEL 4

7. Let κ be a regular uncountable cardinal and let $S \subseteq \kappa$. A function $f : S \to \kappa$ is said to be **regressive** if $\forall\alpha(\alpha \neq 0 \to f(\alpha) < \alpha)$. Suppose that every regressive function $f : S \to \kappa$ is constant on an unbounded subset of S. Prove that S is stationary.

Proof: Suppose toward contradiction that S is nonstationary. Let $C \subseteq \kappa$ be a club such that $C \cap S = \emptyset$. Define $f : C \to \kappa$ by $f(\alpha) = \bigcup(C \cap \alpha)$. Then $f(\alpha) < \alpha$. So, f is regressive. Since C is closed, for each $\alpha < \kappa$, $f(\alpha) \in C$. For each $\beta < \kappa$, if $\alpha \in C$ is greater than the least element in C above β, then $f(\alpha) > \beta$. So, f does not have the same value for κ many α's, contradicting our assumption. $\qquad\square$

8. Let κ be a regular uncountable cardinal, let $S \subseteq \kappa$ be a stationary set, and let $f: S \to \kappa$ be regressive. Prove that there is a stationary set $A \subseteq S$ and $\beta < \kappa$ such that $f[A] = \{\beta\}$.

Proof: Suppose toward contradiction that there is no such stationary set. Then for each $\beta < \kappa$, let C_β be a club such that $C_\beta \cap f^{-1}[\{\beta\}] = \emptyset$. Let $D = \{\eta \mid \forall \beta < \eta (\eta \in C_\beta)\}$. By Problem 6, D is a club in κ. If $\gamma \in D \cap S$, then $f(\gamma) \neq \beta$ for all $\beta < \gamma$. This would contradict f being regressive. So, $D \cap S = \emptyset$, contradicting that S is stationary. $\qquad\square$

LEVEL 5

9. Prove that there is a set $S \subseteq \omega_1$ such that both S and $\omega_1 \setminus S$ are stationary.

Proof: Let $C = \{\alpha < \omega_1 \mid \alpha \text{ is a limit ordinal}\}$. Then C is a club in ω_1 (see Problem 1). For each $\alpha \in C$, there is a sequence (α_n) such that $m < n \to \alpha_m < \alpha_n$ and $\alpha = \bigcup\{\alpha_n \mid n < \omega\}$. For each $n < \omega$, define $f_n: C \to \omega_1$ by $f_n(\alpha) = \alpha_n$. For each $n < \omega$ and $\alpha \in C$, $f_n(\alpha) < \alpha$. So, by Problem 8, for each $n < \omega$, there is $\beta_n < \omega_1$ such that the set $S_n = \{\alpha \in C \mid f_n(\alpha) = \beta_n\}$ is stationary.

Suppose toward contradiction, that for all $n < \omega$, the complement of S_n is not stationary. Then for all $n < \omega$, there is a club C_n with $C_n \subseteq S_n$. Therefore, $\bigcap\{C_n \mid n < \omega\} \subseteq \bigcap\{S_n \mid n < \omega\}$. So, the set $\bigcap\{S_n \mid n < \omega\}$ contains an ordinal α such that $\alpha > \bigcup\{\beta_n \mid n < \omega\}$. Then $(\alpha_n) = (f_n(\alpha)) = (\beta_n)$, and so $\bigcup\{\alpha_n \mid n < \omega\} \neq \alpha$, a contradiction.

Therefore, there is $n < \omega$ such that the complement of S_n is stationary. So, the set S_n satisfies our requirements. $\qquad\square$

10. Let D be the following statement: There is a family $\{A_\alpha \mid \alpha < \omega_1\}$, such that for each $\alpha < \omega_1$, $A_\alpha \subseteq \alpha$ and for every $A \subseteq \omega_1$, the set $\{\alpha < \omega_1 \mid A \cap \alpha = A_\alpha\}$ is stationary. Prove that D implies CH.

Proof: Let $\{A_\alpha \mid \alpha < \omega_1\}$ satisfy for each $\alpha < \omega_1$, $A_\alpha \subseteq \alpha$ and $\forall A \subseteq \omega_1$, $\{\alpha < \omega_1 \mid A \cap \alpha = A_\alpha\}$ is stationary. Let $A \subseteq \omega$. Since $\{\alpha < \omega_1 \mid A \cap \alpha = A_\alpha\}$ is stationary and $C = \{\eta \mid \omega < \eta < \kappa\}$ is a club (by Example 16.1), there is $\alpha < \omega_1$ with $\alpha > \omega$ such that $A = A \cap \alpha = A_\alpha$. It follows that $\mathcal{P}(\omega) \subseteq \{\alpha < \omega_1 \mid A \cap \alpha = A_\alpha\}$. Thus, $|\mathcal{P}(\omega)| \leq |\{\alpha < \omega_1 \mid A \cap \alpha = A_\alpha\}| \leq \omega_1$. Since ω_1 is the least uncountable cardinal and $\mathcal{P}(\omega)$ is uncountable, $\omega_1 \leq |\mathcal{P}(\omega)|$. So, $2^\omega = |\mathcal{P}(\omega)| = \omega_1$. $\qquad\square$

About the Author

Dr. Steve Warner, a New York native, earned his Ph.D. at Rutgers University in Pure Mathematics in May 2001. While a graduate student, Dr. Warner won the TA Teaching Excellence Award.

After Rutgers, Dr. Warner joined the Penn State Mathematics Department as an Assistant Professor and in September 2002, he returned to New York to accept an Assistant Professor position at Hofstra University. By September 2007, Dr. Warner had received tenure and was promoted to Associate Professor. He has taught undergraduate and graduate courses in Precalculus, Calculus, Linear Algebra, Differential Equations, Mathematical Logic, Set Theory, and Abstract Algebra.

From 2003 – 2008, Dr. Warner participated in a five-year NSF grant, "The MSTP Project," to study and improve mathematics and science curriculum in poorly performing junior high schools. He also published several articles in scholarly journals, specifically on Mathematical Logic.

Dr. Warner has nearly two decades of experience in general math tutoring and tutoring for standardized tests such as the SAT, ACT, GRE, GMAT, and AP Calculus exams. He has tutored students both individually and in group settings.

In February 2010 Dr. Warner released his first SAT prep book "The 32 Most Effective SAT Math Strategies," and in 2012 founded Get 800 Test Prep. Since then Dr. Warner has written books for the SAT, ACT, SAT Math Subject Tests, AP Calculus exams, and GRE. In 2018 Dr. Warner released his first pure math book called "Pure Mathematics for Beginners." Since then he has released several more books, each one addressing a specific subject in pure mathematics.

Dr. Steve Warner can be reached at

steve@SATPrepGet800.com

BOOKS BY DR. STEVE WARNER

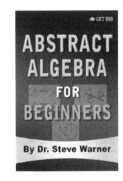

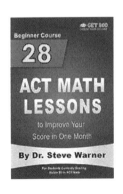

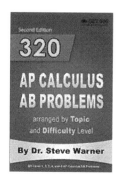

Made in the USA
Coppell, TX
22 December 2019